Point Lobos

Interpretation of a Primitive Landscape

D1470611

STATE OF CALIFORNIA — THE RESOURCES AGENCY
DEPARTMENT OF PARKS AND RECREATION

UNIVERSITY EXTENSION
UNIVERSITY OF CALIFORNIA, BERKELEY

POINT LOBOS
State Reserve

Interpretation of a Primitive Landscape

Originally Edited by
AUBREY DRURY
Revised Edition by
JOSEPH H. ENGBECK JR.

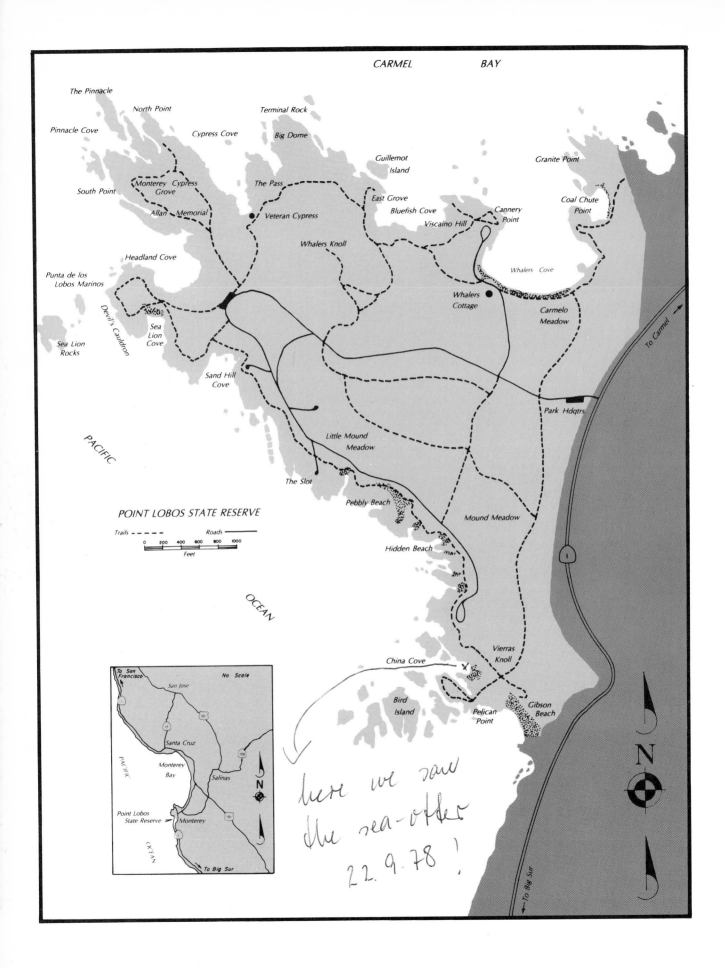

CARMEL BAY

The Pinnacle

North Point

Terminal Rock

Pinnacle Cove

Cypress Cove

Big Dome

Guillemot
Island

Granite Point

Monterey Cypress
Grove

The Pass

East Grove

Coal Chute
Point

South Point

Bluefish Cove

Cannery
Point

Allan Memorial

Veteran Cypress

Viscaino Hill

Whalers Cove

Headland Cove

Whalers Knoll

Punta de los
Lobos Marinos

Whalers
Cottage

Devil's Cauldron

Sea
Lion
Cove

Carmelo
Meadow

Sea Lion
Rocks

To Carmel

Sand Hill
Cove

PACIFIC

Park Hdqtrs.

Little Mound
Meadow

The Slot

POINT LOBOS STATE RESERVE

Pebbly Beach

Trails ------   Roads _____

Mound Meadow

0   200 400 600 800 1000
Feet

Hidden Beach

OCEAN

Vierras
Knoll

China Cove

Gibson
Beach

No Scale

To San
Francisco

Bird
Island

Pelican
Point

San Jose

here we saw
the sea-otter
22.9.78 !

PACIFIC

Santa Cruz

152

Monterey
Bay

Salinas

Point Lobos
State Reserve

Monterey

OCEAN

To Big Sur

To Big Sur

N

Contents

Foreword to the First Edition

Aubrey Drury took special interest in the history of California and the West. He was active with the California Historical Landmarks Committee and various conservation organizations, and served for many years as president of the California Historical Society. When his brother, Newton, was Director of the National Park Service and therefore absent from California, Aubrey Drury served as Administrative Secretary of the Save-the-Redwoods League. He was the author of *California, An Intimate Guide*, co-author of *The Pacific Coast Ranges*, as well as other books and articles. He was the editor of the original version of this book about Point Lobos, and co-author with Mr. Neasham of Chapter X dealing with the history of Point Lobos.

THIS BOOK IS INTENDED to guide the reader to a fuller understanding of Point Lobos Reserve, its unique value as an example of primitive landscape, and the reasons for the policy underlying its administration.

A rocky promontory on the shore of the Pacific three miles south of Carmel, California, crowned by a grove of picturesque wind-blown Monterey cypress, backed by slopes and meadows rich with associations of plant and animal life in relatively undisturbed environment, Point Lobos has long been recognized as an area of rare natural beauty and exceptional scientific interest. When it was acquired for the inspiration and enjoyment of the public, the California State Park Commission appreciated its perishable qualities, and asked an advisory committee, with assistance from the Carnegie Corporation, the Carnegie Institution of Washington, and the Save-the-Redwoods League, to undertake an intensive study of all values inherent in the site, and to recommend the plan upon which the present policy of protection is based. This publication has been made possible by a grant from the Carnegie Institution of Washington, D.C.

A composite work, this volume has been taken from the findings of specialists who contributed to the Point Lobos Master Plan, and the writings of others who have thought upon the problem of protecting primitive landscape conditions. At times these are quoted verbatim, and at other times their reports or recommendations are paraphrased. Credit is given at the beginning of each chapter to those from whose studies material has been drawn.

Just as Point Lobos Reserve is a living, growing thing, subject to never-ending change, so this book may doubtless in future editions undergo extensive modification both in content and method of approach—provided the belief is correct that there is continuing need for such a work in the field of nature interpretation.

August, 1954   *Aubrey Drury*

Foreword

MORE THAN FORTY YEARS have elapsed since the reserve concept was first put into effect at Point Lobos. And during this entire time the masterplan drawn up by the original Point Lobos Advisory Committee has served the area well. Human impact on the natural landscape has remained minimal even though millions of people have visited the area. The cypress groves are flourishing, the woods and meadows are alive with birds and other wildlife, and wildflower displays are incredibly rich and varied. The shoreline teems with life including some species that are now rarely seen in other, less protected portions of the coast. As the years go by the wisdom of the management plan itself becomes ever more obvious and inspirational—living proof that this kind of nature preservation effort can be successful.

Meanwhile the Reserve has grown. In 1959 and 1960 the nation's first marine reserve was established adjacent to Point Lobos, and in 1962 an upland area of pygmy forest was acquired by the State and added to the Reserve. In 1967 Point Lobos was recognized as a National Natural Landmark thus providing additional legal protection for the area, and in 1973 the California Fish and Game Commission gave the marine portion of the area Ecological Reserve Status thus ending all fishing or other consumptive uses there. In 1974 additional land was acquired alongside the northern edge of the Reserve, and as of 1975 expansion of the marine reserve is under consideration.

Throughout this time the basic management programs for Point Lobos have been under continual review in order to ensure that the values identified by the original Point Lobos Advisory Committee were receiving adequate care. With ever increasing numbers of people coming to the Reserve it now appears, for instance, that the use of private motor vehicles within the Reserve will have to be even more sharply limited than was considered necessary in 1935.

In his foreword to the original edition of this book, Aubrey Drury pointed out that "Point Lobos is a living, growing thing, subject to never-ending change," and that this book should therefore be revised and updated as long as there was need for such a tool "in the field of nature interpretation." Far from diminishing with the years, the need for nature interpretation has grown steadily as more and more of our population has come to live in urban environments. And so it has seemed quite appropriate to revise and update the book, though at the same time an effort has been made to preserve the flavor of the original edition, and changes or additions have been made only where they were clearly desirable. In the 1970 revised edition of the book, for instance, the chapter on geology was expanded to include more of the information developed by the original advisory committee. Also in 1970 a chapter on the marine reserve and biographical notes about the authors were added and the entire book was redesigned using new photographs to go along with the best of the old ones.

The current edition of this book is the result of a cooperative effort between the California Department of Parks and Recreation and University Extension, University of California, Berkeley. This publication represents a kind of homecoming for the book in that almost all of the original contributors to the book were either students or faculty members of the University of California. The Reserve itself owes its creation in large measure to the vision and dedication of leading conservationists who were closely associated with the University—men such as John Merriam, William Colby, Newton Drury, and others.

It is appropriate, moreover, that this book should now be made more widely available through a cooperative effort between the Department of Parks and Recreation and the University of California. For now as we enter the last quarter of the twentieth century an increasing number of people are convinced that the most profoundly important question facing humanity is whether or not our species can live in harmony with the natural world. This matter—of concern to humanity over the long term—must be dealt with by educational institutions on all levels including those great universities that have serious and thoughtful programs of continuing education for adults. For in a free society millions of people must participate in basic decisions about social, economic, and environmental matters, and if we are to act wisely we must be able to look outside ourselves, must be concerned with far more than our own personal interests of the moment.

The astonishing beauty of Point Lobos has the power to entice people out of their private preoccupations and into a deep appreciation of the natural world. This book seeks to transform that appreciation into the more profound and lasting pleasure that comes of knowing something about the story *behind* the scenery. There is joy in this kind of knowledge, in being able to visualize the grandly ongoing process of evolution. And there is a unique kind of serenity in the realization that one is an integral part of nature, of life on an immense scale.

Merriam, Colby, Drury and the others were well aware during the 1930s of the need for this kind of enlightenment, this progression from joy to wisdom. Now, through this publication, and through related programs of education and interpretation, we must go on building on what they began, making sure that the unique and undefiled landscape of Point Lobos is enjoyed not just for its scenic qualities, but also for its ability to enlighten—to inspire joy and wisdom.

October, 1975

I

Protection of the Primitive

John Campbell Merriam

John Campbell Merriam was a distinguished paleontologist, educator, and administrator. A professor of paleontology and Dean of the Faculties at the University of California, Berkeley, he left the University to become president of the Carnegie Institution of Washington, D.C. He was the author of several books and numerous articles in the fields of paleontology, historical geology, the administration of higher education, and advanced research. He was one of the founders of the Save-the-Redwoods League, and a long time president of that organization. His spirited search for knowledge about the history of life on Earth, his vision, leadership, and unconquerable idealism combined to inspire the League, scientists, conservationists, and others to greater accomplishment than would have been possible without him.

WHEN THE PROGRAM FOR PRESERVATION of Point Lobos was being outlined, the primary reason for preserving the area was the occurrence there of the last original or primitive stand of an interesting and beautiful tree, the Monterey cypress. While the Point has many exceptional features, it is doubtful whether the supreme effort to protect it would have been possible without a sharp focus on the need to protect this species of cypress. Of course the association and interrelationship of many other factors were also important—the peculiar charm of the locality, the exceptional esthetic value of the trees themselves, and the magnificent setting of the cypress grove on a rocky promontory almost surrounded by the sea. But it is important to remember that if the Monterey cypress were lost we would have failed in the first purpose of this endeavor.

Of course many other values should be considered in any thoughtful discussion of Point Lobos, and these features should be examined both collectively and as separate units. It should be borne in mind, among other things, that an attempt to maintain the cypress in a primitive condition probably requires maintenance of its original environment. To risk the loss of any element in the setting might jeopardize the whole group, including the cypress. And also it is important to maintain the entire group of elements because such protection not only preserves great scientific values, but at the same time guarantees continuity of esthetic qualities and the human appeal of the region.

The problem of Point Lobos and the Monterey cypress should be considered in the light of our entire store of knowledge about the history of life. In the almost infinitely long period during which life existed on the earth before the appearance of man, a vast number of species of plants and animals became extinct through the influence of natural processes. The history of the Monterey cypress suggests that this tree may, in the geological sense, be on the verge of extinction. If it be true that this species is about to disappear under the influence of natural processes, intensive scientific study might show the manner in which we could rescue this element of beauty and scientific interest by modifying or eliminating some factors inimical to the life of the tree. Viewing the situation from another angle, it may be that we should look upon maintenance of the present natural factors and their natural balance as necessary for maintenance of the cypress as a part of an inextricably interrelated group of natural elements.

The interior of the cypress grove can be hauntingly somber and lonely with its hanging strands of lace-lichen, and sea fog moving slowly through the tree tops.

The Pinnacle.

The Point Lobos project, and the master plan formulated for the California State Park Commission by the Point Lobos Advisory Committee and the associated group of specialists, of course involved attempts to secure information as to all of the natural features at Point Lobos which have human interest or appeal. An exceptional aspect of this program was the effort to bring together data obtained by specialists in many fields of knowledge. This information was brought together in a way that made it possible to look at each feature of the area from many points of view and in terms of many kinds of knowledge. The various features of Point Lobos were examined from the point of view of art, esthetic appreciation, zoology, botany, ecology, geology, paleontology, archeology, and early human history. Consideration was then given to the extent to which these factors conflicted, or the extent to which they could be fitted together in a mosaic program for Point Lobos that was made more valuable or more beautiful because of this interlocking of different elements.

While a program of this nature, using these ideas, does not seem to have been specifically worked out before for any area, the general view of nature as a mosaic of many elements has been considered by writers in various fields. I particularly like to remember the treatment of this idea in Heine's "Die Harzreise."

Monterey cypress is now found growing naturally in only two places—at the western tip of the Monterey Peninsula and at Point Lobos on this rocky promontory almost completely surrounded by the sea.

Monterey cypress has survived vast geologic and biologic change.
In the last century it has been planted in many parts of the world.
However, in its wild and natural state it is now making a
last stand on these high bluffs at the edge of the continent.

In developing those facilities that had to do with human administration and use of Point Lobos, it was necessary to determine the influence of such facilities upon the future value of the area.

It is extremely interesting to note the way in which landscape architects have considered those elements of Point Lobos which have special human interest or value. This is the approach that landscape men should take in consideration of a primitive area, which is to ask, first of all, what are the elements that have human value? These will perhaps rest upon elements other than those ordinarily involved in landscape study. They may be features of geology or natural

history that can, if one knows and understands something about them, have esthetic value comparable to those elements of design or pattern that are commonly used as a basis of judgment by landscape architects.

The study of Point Lobos has been approached by the method which is natural, normal, and necessary, namely determining first what the values are in the area and then making a decision as to how the area should be made accessible and how it may be used. From this study, educational facilities and programs can be developed in order to tell visitors something about the diverse elements that have been discovered through intensive appraisal of the region's values.

*The clean, heavily weathered texture of cypress and granite stands in stark
contrast to the churning surf and dark blue sea surrounding Guillemot Island.*

II

A Master Plan for the Future

Newton B. Drury

Newton B. Drury, an important figure in the American conservation movement, played a vital role in the early activities of the Save-the-Redwoods League and has been active with that organization since 1919. In 1929 he became executive secretary to the California State Park Commission, remaining in that position until 1940 when he became director of the National Park Service. In 1951 he returned to California to once again direct the growth and development of the state's park system. After retiring from that position in 1959 he resumed an active role with the Save-the-Redwoods League. He was secretary to the Point Lobos Advisory Committee at the time of its original study and report. This chapter is based on an article written by Mr. Drury for *American Forests* magazine in 1938.

T*HE GREATEST MEETING OF LAND AND WATER IN THE WORLD.* Extravagant praise for any one portion of the earth's surface; yet these are the words of a noted student of landscape, the painter Francis McComas. And there are many who agree that on Point Lobos there have been brought to a distinguished climax many elements that make for landscape beauty and significance.

Deriving its name from the colonies of sea lions whose hoarse barkings are carried inland from the offshore rocks, *Punta de los Lobos Marinos,* Point of the Sea Wolves, has scientific interest because the habitats of two species of sea lions — California and Steller — here overlap; because it currently[1] features the most northerly breeding place of the California brown pelican; and because many forms of land and marine life remain here undisturbed, in remarkable relationship to their environment and to each other. But the outstanding distinction of the Point unquestionably lies in the presence here of the most outstanding natural grove of *Cupressus macrocarpa,* the Monterey cypress. Widely distributed in earlier geological time, this tree is now, at least in its natural state, making a last stand in the Monterey region. Clinging precariously to the cliffs above the surf, shaped into picturesque forms by wind and weather, shrouded sometimes in the smoke of drifting fog, the living trees rich green in foliage, the dead ones standing stark in silhouette, their bleached white twisted branches red with algae, these cypresses are the characteristic note in this landscape — a landscape long beloved of artists for its form and color, and the dramatic story revealed by its oceanward pinnacles — the neverending conflict between sea and land.

It was the recognition of such distinction that inspired the State of California, after long negotiations and at considerable cost, to acquire Point Lobos in order to preserve it as part of the nation's heritage of beauty.

Escaping almost miraculously from the destruction of native landscape values that had occurred around it, passing from owner to owner who regarded it lightly — once in the free-and-easy early days of the Mexican regime, tradition says, lost as the stake in a game of cards — site of a whaling station, shipment point for a coal mine, laid out on paper as a townsite with a harsh gridiron of streets, grazed over by cattle, in parts occasionally burned — this rare and exceptional landscape was finally possessed by an owner who appreciated its full value; and, when it passed into the trusteeship of the State of California, fortunately held most of the essentially primitive character that had lured increasing thousands to it.

Yet when the State acquired Point Lobos, apprehension as to its future still remained.

Residents of Carmel, a quaint and leisurely village which had long been a refuge for votaries of the arts, held up their hands in horror at the prospect of a *state park*. They envisioned formal paths and artificial masonry, networks of roads and the frantic rush of automobile traffic, the din of crowds, the nondescript structures of catch-penny concessions and tourist camps, all, they feared, to the loss of more precious, but more fragile things—the spell, the mystery, the beauty of this site.

The Carmelites sighed with relief, therefore, and so did nature lovers throughout the nation, when the State Park Commission set its face against these possibilities, pledging for all time that Point Lobos would be a "reserve"—a property held in trust as nature had designed it. For the commission concluded that it was in the public interest to hold this land unmodified, even at the cost of considerable restriction of use, as thus only could its highest values to the public be perpetuated.

Even so, the declaration of such a policy was not enough. What were the values? How could they be protected for people of many generations to enjoy? To find an answer to these questions was the complex problem confronting the commission.

Gladly, therefore, they availed themselves of the offer of the Save-the-Redwoods League, with financial assistance from the Carnegie Corporation and the Carnegie Institution of Washington, to make a thorough study, to formulate a policy, and to recommend a plan. An advisory committee of scientists, artists and conservationists was formed, with Dr. Ray Lyman Wilbur of Stanford University as its chairman. Specialists in many fields were engaged to make sustained observations, and to prepare an inventory, as it were, of all values possessed by Point Lobos, both material and intangible. Frequent conferences were held on the ground by the committee and its advisers, to determine the interrelation and proper evaluation of all the findings. It was not enough to map the topography, to analyze the geological structures, to plot the vegetative cover, to chronicle the 400 or more species of plants, 178 species of vertebrate animals, eighty-eight species of marine invertebrates along the shore and in the tidal pools, the many species of seaweed and marine algae. The normal balance of conditions favorable to the persistence of each plant and animal species had to be studied. More, the relation of this balance to human use of the area had to be gauged.

Geologists, zoologists, botanists, foresters, ecologists, plant pathologists, and even archeologists and historians each contributed significant information. They plotted and analyzed the esthetic effects involved in the pattern and composition of the landscape. They studied the forces, both natural and artificial, that might tend to lessen or destroy the overall quality produced by many interrelated factors.

It took two years to prepare an 850-page typewritten volume embodying these reports and studies. Frederick Law Olmsted, well-known landscape architect, and his co-worker, George B. Vaughn, were asked to correlate the findings within a plan designed to afford visitors to Point Lobos the maximum enjoyment of its most worthwhile values while causing a minimum of disturbance to natural conditions.

The Park Commission and the Advisory Committee had before them ample warnings. They had observed the fate of other celebrated California landscapes whose fame and popularity had carried the seeds of their destruction. In their own state parks in the coast redwoods of Humboldt County, for instance, the roadside had been steadily conventionalized and cheapened, as increasing pressure of tourist traffic had induced "improvement" of the Redwood Highway; at the Big Basin Redwoods of Santa Cruz County, the central grove of which a generation ago was rich in all the attributes of the primitive, the forest floor carpeted with ferns and flowering plants; but which today [1938], frequented by milling throngs, cluttered with structures strangely out of place among the stately redwoods, presents an aspect bare as the ground beneath a circus tent.[2] In the California Sierra, wilderness values were everywhere being rapidly destroyed as, one after another, the last fastnesses were penetrated by automobile roads. Even in Yosemite, still incomparable, the commission was witness to the steady and inexorable operation of the law of diminishing returns, the disappearance when sought by many of qualities which in the past had given Yosemite its fame. The dictum of Robert Burns, that

> . . . *pleasures are like poppies spread,*
> *You seize the flower, the bloom is sped,*

surely states the situation of some of our greatest areas of natural beauty in California.

What to do—or not to do—in a democracy, in order to perpetuate for the public of today and tomorrow, in undiminished freshness, the perishable qualities of its own property?

That was the delicate question to which the members of the Point Lobos Advisory Committee addressed themselves. Observing trends elsewhere in the same field, they determined to escape if possible some pitfalls into which others had fallen. They promised themselves that they would try to avoid some fetishes that had been set up in the administering of public lands; to resist the pressure of *scenic showmanship* which measures success in revenue or attendance; of *recreational enthusiasm*, which considers that piece of level land wasted which is not teeming with citizens engaged in healthful and innocent outdoor sports, regardless of their appropriateness to the site; of *virtuosity*, the aim of which is to "paint the lily" or remake nature's design in keeping with the preconceived notions of well-meaning individuals or groups, for the glory of themselves and their techniques—or merely to satisfy an itch to monkey with a landscape; of *make-work projects*, exulting in new-found resources, more designed for expenditure of money than expenditure of thought; of that *pseudo-democratic philosophy* which holds that if a piece of property belongs to the public, they have an inalienable and limitless right to use it, even if they use it up.

Extreme as some of these things sound, they all represent tendencies that have lessened the real value of public properties grouped loosely under the term of "parks." This has not occurred through any lack of efficiency in operation on the part of those in charge. It has been largely due to the absence of a clear-cut realization of policy and purpose of administering natural areas.

To remedy such a situation the California State Park Commission adopted the Point Lobos Master Plan.

"To keep at a high level of perfection the unique natural

conditions upon which the greatest values of Point Lobos depend, in order to make these permanently available for the enjoyment, education, and inspiration of the public."

Thus was the purpose stated, and thus was the policy determined, both for development and use. Its guiding principle was moderation. Existing conditions were to be changed as little as possible, and these only in the interest of restoring naturalness or checking destructive tendencies. Automobile roads, for instance, were reduced from 16,000 to 8,000 feet, and their scars removed, without lessening their main function of carrying visitors within reasonable distance of important points. Parking places were located after careful study.[3]

The finer areas were to be entered only on foot, over unobtrusive trails following the logical course of travel to those features of greatest beauty and interest, as determined by the analysis of the property. As a protective measure a small day use fee was recommended by the commission. It was felt that such a fee would have the threefold merit of providing some revenue for administration, of being nominal for those who are genuinely interested, and of giving enhanced appreciation of an experience through having paid for it. Long experience in these matters indicates that marauders of the landscape do not so readily mobilize on foot.

Camping and gatherings of the convention type, because of their destructive effects, were not authorized. Rules against destruction of plant and animal life are explained and interpreted by the staff, as well as enforced. Protection from extreme hazard required that there be no fires or smoking. "Clean-up" for fire protection or other purposes has been practiced with restraint. The scientists have discovered important functions of the brush and grasslands as the habitat for small mammals and many species of birds. Structures and all artificial intrusions have been kept to the minimum necessary for administration, and so placed that they will not mar any important element in the picture.

As to protection, one emergency has already been revealed by the studies of plant pathologists. It is the threat of the cypress canker, deadly foe of the Monterey cypress, which if it takes hold at Point Lobos will destroy the most distinctive feature. Discovery of this plant disease within two miles of the Reserve led to definite and aggressive measures. Trained crews furnished by the National Park Service Civilian Conservation Corps combed the territory for at least ten miles around to detect and remove from all plantations of Monterey cypress those diseased trees from which the spores might be transmitted by wind or birds, and a protective zone was established wherein systematic examination and eradication were carried on.

Already in many parts of California the planted cypresses, so important in our landscape, are believed to be doomed, so far had this disease advanced before its menace was realized. There is no discovered cure. It may be that in its type of locality the Monterey cypress will make its last stand, saved only in Point Lobos Reserve from total extinction.

All this, and much more, in the way of protective procedure is being interpreted and explained to the visiting public, and embodied in a basic publication. Artists, writers, students of flora and fauna are encouraged to make this their headquarters, so that steadily at Point Lobos there may grow a tradition favorable to the established objectives. As to re-

This aerial photograph was taken shortly before the Reserve was established. The old highway and Bassett Avenue both show clearly as do the mounds in Mound Meadow and numerous trails through the grassland areas.

sults from the Point Lobos program, California park authorities are optimistic and encouraged. Success thus far has been assured by the complete understanding and sympathy of the state park administrators. Their plans have been carried out ably by successive Reserve supervisors. Scientists and others who contributed to the plan, upon revisiting the area, are impressed by the progress thus far in maintaining and restoring natural conditions. Displays of spring wildflowers in the undisturbed meadows and on grassy slopes were never more colorful. Marine life in the tidal pools along the coast remains in undiminished interest. The pine woods inland are a refuge for the many creatures whose presence gives meaning to the total spectacle. That mosaic involving important human values as spoken of by Dr. John C. Merriam, "a mosaic of many elements" in a primitive natural setting, is being held intact, we hope, for countless generations to enjoy.

Certain it is that the Point Lobos study, master plan, and program have significance, not only in determining the future trend here, but in setting the pattern for the administration of certain other possessions in the California park system. Of course, not all of California's state parks are destined to be "reserves." Some have historic meaning, primarily; some will be devoted to outdoor recreation—the ocean beaches of the south for instance. But for the more perishable areas within the State Park System, the program at Point Lobos has pointed the way to sound procedure, based on knowledge and appreciation. It has emphasized the fact that it takes time and thought—coupled with a clear conception of objectives—to provide for protection of primitive qualities in the native landscape.

1—This statement remained true until roughly 1960. For further information see Chapter VIII, section on pelicans.

2—The conditions mentioned by Mr. Drury were finally corrected by a series of physical and administrative changes accomplished in the years between 1960 and 1968.

3—The original plan for automotive access and parking worked well for many years. However, in 1970 with visitation at Point Lobos approaching 200,000 persons per year the old plan no longer fully accomplishes its original intent. Now a new plan is being considered that would give increased emphasis to the Reserve's educational and inspirational values and perhaps eliminate automotive traffic and parking problems altogether.

"The timeless battering and grinding of the sea upon the shore is one of the most powerful, persistent, and dramatic of the natural processes characteristic of Point Lobos." — Frederick Law Olmsted Jr.

III

A Landscape of Beauty & Meaning

Frederick Law Olmsted Jr. / George B. Vaughan

Frederick Law Olmsted Jr., an outstanding and nationally acclaimed landscape architect, directed the official 1927-29 California State Park Survey. This work was a crucial part of the effort to establish a statewide system of parks. He and his firm also did design and survey work for the National Park Service and for many other local, state, and national agencies. In 1945 the California legislature set aside $15 million for state park acquisition, and Mr. Olmsted was again retained by the State Park Commission to do a supplementary survey of state park needs.

George B. Vaughan, as part of his assignment with the Olmsted Brothers firm of landscape architects, spent some seventeen months at Point Lobos and was the official representative of the Point Lobos Advisory Committee. Much of this chapter is based on his intensive investigations of Point Lobos. He also gave valuable assistance to many of the other research projects that were eventually included in the original Point Lobos Advisory Committee's Report.

WHEN THE SEAS ARE RUNNING HIGH, as they so often do at Point Lobos, the huge waves, with their heaving, burst and drag, grip the attention and rouse the emotions. This spectacular impact upon shore forms of extraordinary variety stirs the mind to some appreciation of the vast power and dramatic quality of the forces here at work. But on every hand, and in every kind of weather, other phases of the same great drama first become apparent, and then become more and more impressive as one's understanding grows.

The functional adaptation of this area's richly varied marine and littoral vegetation is directly traceable to the impact of waves and currents, of ocean winds and windborne spray and spume and fog—from the lithe seaweed up through the tapestries of rock plants to the gnarled cypresses and the wind-molded pines.

The cypresses tell a poignant story of survival in a battle against great odds, twisting and buttressing themselves against the thrust of wind and pull of gravity, extracting vigor from the driving sea fogs and adapting themselves to drenching sprays of salt that sometimes crust the soil with white and rout the advance of other trees.

Whole communities of living things are shaped in every vital detail to play their strenuous parts in the everlasting drama of the sea and shore—visibly so shaped, not only in response to these pervasive forces of sea and wind but also in response to conditions of soil and rock which are themselves the outcome of the same unending reaction of sea and land.

Rocks now crumble visibly before the eyes, grain after grain; rocks plainly formed in long-past ages out of pebbles on beaches, not unlike the present, then buried deep until a new uplifting of the continent enabled the sea to cut those other less ancient beaches which we see on the present hillsides, terrace below terrace—until finally the ocean again reached and hammered into the same old beach conglomerate, rattling its veteran pebbles back and forth, and with them battering out new clefts, chasms and caves where planes of weakness had been formed by continental heavings.

Infinite are the variations of meaning relating to this single dominant theme, immensely inspiring in their significance, and expressed in forms of exceptional sensual beauty.

One, sensitive to beauty and meaning in landscape, and disposed to analyze its appeal in terms of pattern, form and color, finds in Point Lobos Reserve and surrounding country a great variety of types. An attempt to classify them would reveal as worthy of specialized appreciation such types as: (a) the seaward margins of the cypress grove; (b) the cypress forest interiors; (c) glades and meadows on the cypress forest landward margins; (d) Big Dome cliffs; (e) open points jutting into the sea; (f) the littoral areas and sea caves; (g) open saddles;

(h) high chaparral areas; (i) broad, sweeping meadows bounded by pine forest, chaparral and the sea; (j) pine forest interiors.

It should be admitted that no satisfactory explanation can be given for any esthetic experience, so far as the landscape is concerned. It should also be recognized that the appeal of Point Lobos is to many senses, and is composite in nature. To each beholder some one phase or feature has a special meaning. Nevertheless, it may be of some value to attempt a study of some elements that contribute to the character and charm of the different landscape types in this area.

Seaward Margins of the Cypress Grove

THE MOST DRAMATIC landscape effect—in fact the supreme effect of the entire Reserve—is found on the outer ends of the cypress-covered points, and principally of Cypress Headland. Here, as on a mountaintop, one has the sense of being on a battleground of natural forces where man is a negligible factor. Here, where cypress clings to the very edge of the continent, one can sense quite vividly the power of the elements as the rolling surf churns against jagged rock. The same power is evident in the outline of rock formations sloping upward and away from the sea. And it is there in the similarly sculptured surfaces of the wind-sheared cypress foliage, and goes on back to the crest of the forest, beyond which there is at last comparative shelter. If, when the wind blows, there be driving fog to trace its course, this whole effect is intensified; for the fog drifts up along these same lines, flowing over the sloping rocks and smoothed foliage, and through the bleached and naked limbs of any tree that has dared to raise itself above the general slope. The tree trunks leaning from the wind, foliage clinging in dense masses on the sheltered side of branches, buttress formations to the lee supporting trunks and limbs, and anchor roots to the windward holding fast in crevices of the granite—all these things, even on a quiet day, tell a story of frequent high winds and flying spume.

The feeling of seclusion, of being far removed from the influence of man, is an important part of the spell that is cast by this place. Little is here to remind one of human attempts to modify the work of nature. Trees carry dead branches, and skeletons of trees whose life cycle is completed stand stark or lie prostrate, undisturbed. Here is the inner sanctuary —a sanctuary that is reached by progressively leaving the evidences of civilization behind; first, by turning aside from the main stream of traffic at the highway gate; next, by leaving the supervisor's house (entrance station) behind; then abandoning the automobile at the entrance to the headland, and finally coming on foot through the cypress forest with one's face toward the ocean and the end of land.

Where the oceanward pinnacles burst upon the view, one feels most strongly the stress and flow of elements that result from repetition of form; the slope of rocks repeated again and again, and re-echoed in wind-blown trees and movements of fog; and if one stands on the open end of Cypress Headland this repetition is increased by the view of

The Pinnacle through a "window-vista" in the cypress grove.

three or four rocky points, each in succession presenting a variation of the same theme.

Another interesting repetition of form, conspicuous throughout all the granitic portions of the Reserve and the adjoining coast, is due to various angles and directions of faulting of the granite, a process that has produced a series of steep slopes facing northeasterly and southwesterly. Where a point is being cut off from the mainland by the sea there is also a steep slope to the southeast. The result of all these factors is that the form toward which each point and island is tending as the ocean carves away its base is that of a pyramid. This is typified by the pinnacles at the outer end of Cypress Headland.

Combined with this strong harmony of form is a remarkable richness of color. The sea is the most changeable element, reflecting from afar every color of light thrown upon it; rich blue under a sunny sky, shot with white or lead gray from banks of fog, or tinged by brilliant reds and yellows of a sunset. Close inshore the plunging view from bluffs and cliffs, so characteristic of Point Lobos, penetrates the surface reflections and catches light reflected from things beneath: brilliant emerald greens of sunlit sand, warm red-browns of waving kelp, lavenders and crimsons of various life-forms encrusted on the rocks, rich olive greens of deep water and pale blue-greens of submerged clouds of air close to the foaming white breakers—with, perhaps, as an added touch of color, a black and white guillemot with orange-red feet swimming near the shore. These are impressions one remembers, and when overlaid with swirls of creamy froth and broken here and there by reflected glints of gray rocks, overhanging green foliage, bright orange alga or blue sky, the riotous symphony of changing color becomes a challenge to every artist to see how much of it he can catch. Then add to these the red-browns of the granite below the spray line; and, above, the blue and pink trailing rosettes of succulents (*Dudleya*) with their pale yellow flowers making a soft rich tapestry over the steep bluffs; and, above these, a zone of green covered with fiery orange Indian paint brush (*Castilleja*), bright yellow mock heather (*Haplopappus*) and soft blue sea daisies (*Erigeron*) going back into the shade of the cypress woods where the tree trunks rise, red-brown or bleached gray; some of them naked and dead, others supporting dense tops of twiggage washed beneath with the rich orange-red and silver of the alga; and crowned against the sky with bright green foliage. This is rich pictorial material, and even painters who care little for the manifestations of nature come here day after day, and year after year, for inspiration.

For those interested in observing nature as a dynamic living organism, there is, over and above the thrill of color and form, the living drama of two opposed processes—one, the disintegration of the rock by plant cover, rain and sun, making food for the support of a richer and finer plant cover; and the other, that of the sea eating slowly back into this headland, aided, strangely enough, by the cypress tree itself, which may be observed splitting off great chunks of granite by the pressure of growing roots in seams of the rock. It is thrilling to go out onto the Cypress Headland and stand in a wilderness of clean-washed granite ridges with sea water surging in narrow chasms between and among rocky ribs of the earth that once supported soil, flowers, and trees like those seen inshore.

The cycle of growth and decay of the cypress is worth noting because of its influence on the character of this landscape. Where reproduction is very thin and scattered, as on the outlying ridges at the end of Cypress Headland, and in portions of the landward margins, trees stand out as individuals through their entire history. Elsewhere, reproduction is apt to go in waves, creating thickets of young cypresses whose foliage often presents continuous surfaces modeled by the wind into smooth-flowing contours. The most outstanding examples of this effect are to be found in the eastern portion of the north shore. A less extensive example is to be found at the head of the southern cove on the end of Cypress Headland. As such a group matures, losing its lower limbs, it approaches the condition of the much painted and photographed group of twisted and distorted trees on the outer south side of Cypress Headland which is of added significance when one realizes that this represents a late stage in the life of this group. Where reproduction has been adequate to insure the continuance of such groups, rapidly growing young trees have obscured the old picturesque trees.

Another of the outstanding cypress forms is found also on the seaward margins, but on more sheltered portions of the shore is splendidly typified by the so-called *Old Veteran* at the head of the cove west of Little Dome. Old, flat-topped trees of this type have matured without much distortion from wind, standing mostly alone at the seaward edge of open meadows where they form striking silhouettes against the sea beyond. On the south shore of Cypress Headland, such trees compose magnificent pictures with the meadow in the foreground and the farther side of Headland Cove and the Seal Rocks as a backdrop.

*Northeast-facing granite
cliffs above Cypress Cove.
The Veteran Cypress and
Whalers Knoll are in the background.*

Cypress Forest Interiors

OF THIS PHASE there are at least two classifications: (1) Dense thickets of young trees, usually with many dead twigs and of little esthetic value as seen from within—they have important meaning, however, as they are one link in the development cycle of the cypress; (2) Heavy, mature groves containing large trees. Such groves have considerable dignity if they are not too cluttered with small, young growth, although some inmixing of young trees gives interest and contrast. Since these groves are limited in extent, it is always possible to get glimpses of the bright sea out between the trunks. Thus although one feels sheltered from the sea-winds and bright light while in these groves, nevertheless the eye is drawn toward the sea margins visible through the many fine "vista windows." As a result, these groves are less restful and sufficient in themselves than are the depths of the pine forest. The principal interests here are the great variety of fine tree shapes and the vistas seen through them. Notable groups of large specimens are scattered through the cypress areas, each with a character of its own. In several places the character and interest in the cypress woods lie in the trailing lace-lichen hanging pale green and moss-like from every branch and twig, usually lighted from beyond through the filmy shreds. This adds to the atmosphere of "untouched wilderness."

Glades and Meadows of the Cypress Forest Landward Margins

OPEN MARGINS of the cypress forest, away from the sea and sheltered spaces or glades within the woods, whatever their cause, are very important to the total esthetic makeup of the cypress areas. Views across these openings reveal the luxuriant green walls of cypress foliage, along with vistas

The west side of Big Dome.
Cypress trees can be seen
growing erect and tall where
they are protected from the wind.

of the sea, and surf-battered rocks crowned with wind-dwarfed trees. Here we have the contrast of two phases of cypress growth. It is difficult to associate the battered cypresses of the outer rocks with the same trees thriving richly on the edges of sheltered inland swales. Such amazingly different forms are assumed under different conditions.

The distributional pattern of the cypress grove, typically a crescent with its thick middle portion on the outer end of a granitic point and the two tapering points trailing back toward the heads of coves on either side, follows largely the pattern of fog penetration when being "burned off" by the sun over the heated land, and also the pattern which one would expect a given density of salt from the breakers to penetrate under similar conditions of sea-winds—and thus to the beauty of the scene is added the interest of speculating about the factors that have so reduced the once-extensive cypress forests to their present slight hold on the two granitic points they now occupy.

Big Dome Cliffs

THE NORTH SIDE of Big Dome and the adjacent shore, while bearing cypress, are quite different in feeling from the other cypress areas because of the dramatic cliffs rising almost sheer from the water in bare faces of beautiful lichen-covered granite, with only narrow footholds here and there for trees, to the narrow summit, 260 feet above sea-level. Here, though confined to the shelves where soil can lodge, the cypress has propagated continuously so that in any location the trees range from magnificent, tall, straight-shafted giants to graceful, pointed seedlings a few inches to a few feet in height. Here, instead of finding the trees distorted and dwarfed from battling with the salt-laden wind, we find them high up above the sea thriving against the background of colorful rocks which shelter them from both sun and wind. Because of the northern exposure, the rocks are always a show of color from herbaceous material. Here, too, are a few adventurous pines that have seeded into a habitat where they can never thrive. Some may feel that these sickly trees weaken the otherwise admirable effect created by the other plants which so well adapt themselves to these cool, rocky shelves. Nevertheless these pines are of considerable ecological interest.

Open Points Jutting Into the Sea

THERE ARE THREE such points of outstanding quality: Pelican Point, Punta de los Lobos Marinos, and Granite Point. From the former two the central objects of interest are nesting birds, seals, sea lions, and now with their return from near extinction—the playful sea otter.[1]

From Pelican Point the effects are comparatively simple: the bare, knobby islands with the wash of the sea about their feet, and several species of birds departing and birds arriving making everchanging patterns in the sky. Morning is a time for zoological study. Evening is a time of silhouettes.

From Punta de los Lobos Marinos the interest is more

A unique, natural color effect can be seen along this northeast side of Cypress Point, where orange-red algae cling to the dead twigs and trunks of the cypress. This alga, Chroolepus, is related to the sea weeds, and is one of the few algae that have adapted themselves to life in moisture-laden air. It is harmless to the trees, and occurs almost exclusively where the cypress trees are within reach of the salt-laden sea spray on north-easterly exposures. It is most impressive at day's end, when its own vivid coloration is heightened by the golden-red light of the setting sun.

The feeling of seclusion, of being far removed from the influence of man, is an important part of the spell that is cast by Point Lobos State Reserve.

varied and the scene more changing. The great sea lions keep calling attention to themselves with their yelping and growling as they spar on the rocks or sport in the breakers. [Sea otters can often be seen here, too. Generally they will be found playing or feeding along the edge of the kelp beds alternately diving to reach their food supply on the rocky ocean floor, and then surfacing to eat. Often they can be spotted by the sound they make as they float on their backs, using a small rock as a kind of anvil in order to break open the shell of a turban snail or large mussel or other food item brought up from the rocky bottom.]

Here, during a high surf, the great seas, crashing over the rocks and charging down on the outer end of the Point, leap high into the air and fall back again in a drenching rain. Here, on a quiet day and at low tide, one may see tide pools filled with many kinds of living things and lovely as any garden. And here at close intervals, all day long, sea birds pass, flying north or south between the Point and the Seal Rocks, so that one might well sit for long hours watching the movement of the sea and the life associated with it.

In the northeast corner of the Reserve, Granite Point presents quite a different appeal. All through the spring much of the area is covered with the most colorful wildflower display to be found in the Reserve, both of the rocky meadow types and those of the north-facing sea-bluffs. Over these, as a foreground, one gets raking views of the whole north shore with its picturesque knobs and bumps, its outlying islands and its cypresses and pines. To the east, against a background of curving beaches, hills, and valleys, is the string of rocky reefs close by across Moss Cove, where one may see as fine a surf as any to be found in this area. One may also be impressed by the fact that the topography of this point, its orientation, and plant list (with the exception of tree cover) are all surprisingly like that of Cypress Headland.

Littoral Area

THE PRINCIPAL ESTHETIC VALUE of the littoral, or tidal area, is not usually to be found in the broader outlooks but in the interest of details close at hand.

Of interesting tidal pools containing garden-like growths of plant and animal life, there are quite a number. Notable ones are situated at Sea Lion Point, the Slot, and at Pebbly Beach.

There are a number of small sea caves in Sand Hill Cove and along the coast 1000 and 1500 feet southwesterly. Some of these caves show very beautiful incrustations of lavender and scarlet growths, and most of them give interesting geologic exhibits in clean-ground conglomerate surfaces, often revealing faults that have cracked and slipped the porphyritic pebbles. Of tunnels and double-ended caves (always dramatic evidence of the work of the sea in detaching islands) there are some fifteen in the Reserve. A very interesting one is in East Grove, with a great cypress tree growing on its bridge. The others are mostly grouped near Pelican Point.

Some of the small beaches of the Reserve are tucked away between cliffs, and one happens upon them in surprise. This is true of Gibson Beach and particularly of Hidden Beach and China Beach. The latter is the safest and most sheltered place for swimming. [As of 1970 China Beach is the only place within the Reserve where swimming is permitted.]

Open Saddles

THE LANDSCAPES of the various open saddles in the Reserve are quite varied in character. Of these, perhaps the most interesting is the saddle between Big Dome and Whalers Knoll known as *The Pass*. Looking through it in either direction, one gets much the feeling that one does from looking through a high mountain pass. The bare rocky spur to the south, always colorful with flowers, descends to the strip of meadow in the bottom, in a graceful sweep of lupine, and opposite, Big Dome rises in tiers of pine and cypress which reveal their craggy footing, while through the pass to the east

only the tops of tall pines and cypresses are visible. Climbing up out of the woods from the east, one views Little Dome, interestingly enframed by The Pass with a glimpse of Cypress Headland and the open ocean beyond.

Ecologically, The Pass is one of the most remarkable spots in the Reserve; for here tremendous differences in exposure to sun, wind, and sea fog, as well as wide differences in soil depth and runoff, are all found in one small area. As a result many species are located here and remain in constant competition: the two major trees, large and small shrubs, and several distinct meadow types. Here also is perhaps the finest specimen of mature cypress, neither crowded nor windblown.

The other open saddle to the south of Whalers Knoll is notable because of its broad sweeping views over meadows. That between Vierras Knoll and the knoll to the southwest is remarkable for two smashing "views out" obtainable, at their best, from within a few feet of the edge of the sea bluffs. Here one's eyes move from the picturesque knobs of the Bird Rocks, viewed between pines and flower-decorated crags, to the sudden and thrilling discovery of the gleaming white, and hitherto quite hidden, China Beach beneath, with the surf breaking on it from the pale emerald green water of the narrow granite-bordered cove.

From the saddle, east of Vierras Knoll, one gains sweeping views of the whole south shore to Sand Hill and Whalers Knoll, over a foreground of meadow which is rapidly filling up with bushes and young pines. This fine view, unless something soon arrests the growth, is doomed to disappear.

The open saddle south of Whalers Knoll is fine because of its views over the meadows, with foregrounds variously broken by scattered shrubs and pines. The western view is terminated by the shore and the horizon, the eastern by pine woods and the mountains, with a glimpse of Carmelo Cove.

High Chaparral Areas

WHILE THE NARROW BELTS of high chaparral, made up principally of Ceanothus, are chiefly important esthetically in their relation to the broad meadow views, they have, nevertheless, an interest and charm definitely their own. They constitute an "elfin forest" of weirdly formed "trees" full of small animal and bird life, where wood rat nests are quite a common feature. There soil is a deep soft duff, at times so deep that it takes a lot of heavy rain to penetrate it, so that often there is little or no plant cover.

Broad Sweeping Meadows Bounded by Pine Forest, Chaparral, and the Sea

THE FEELING OF THESE MEADOWS is one of peace and restfulness. They are large enough to give the eye scope to wander, sufficiently contained by their barriers of forest so that one is not wondering what is over the hill; simple in texture, simple in topography, leading the eye inevitably, though gently, to the restful horizon of the sea.

Of pictorial material the meadows are full, although not

One of the massive old pines on Viscaino Hill.

with the lavish richness of the north headland area. Color there is in plenty, in bold splashes throughout the spring when most of the flowers are blooming, and in more subdued but still rich tones of browns and reds throughout the long dry summer, changing with the winter rains to lush bright green shot through with the red-brown of last year's stalks; with always the little-changing foil of dull green pines, almost the dullest green of all the pines, and the everchanging sky and sea. Pictorial depth, that separation of planes of relative distance into sufficiently simple terms to be easily grasped and enjoyed in a single view, is furnished here by the undulating forest margins and by lone trees or isolated clumps of trees standing free in the meadows, between or beyond which more pines are seen at greater distances, carrying the eye through from group to group until it comes to rest on some feature adequate to arrest it. This effect is lovely if the terminus is still more pines, but the striking views, and those most typical of Point Lobos, occur when interest is finally focused on surf-washed shore or bold rocky islands.

Beautiful as these sea-facing meadows are from a purely pictorial standpoint, they become infinitely more inspiring when one knows something of their significance in the long progression of natural change. One may be thrilled by the knowledge that the beautiful front of the meadow, gently sloping toward the sea, represents the cutting and building of a terrace by that same Pacific Ocean which now rolls against the rocks at its seaward margin, and that the surrounding ridge on which perhaps stand pines is the older line of shore-cliff softened by erosion to gentle well-drained slopes where a succession of plants has built nourishing soil from the crumbling rocks until the forest now stands, held by the poorer drainage of the flat meadow, on a line often closely following the line of the ancient sea cliffs.

For flower displays of blazing color, the great meadow southeast of Whalers Knoll is outstanding, with golden poppies in March, contrasted with blue Ceanothus on the margins; in the show of splashes of red-brown Rumex in May and the intermixed blue and pink and yellow of Sisyrinchium, Sidalcea, and Oenothera, lovely close to, but perhaps most effective from the edges of the meadow, making vibrant variations in the reds and maroons of the Rumex. For interesting compositions, for a study of the old beach line and an undisturbed condition of forest margin and meadow flora, and for the interesting mound formation that is typical of the wet meadows in the Reserve, the big Mound Meadow on the south shore is most typical. Here the meadow has never been plowed and the evidence of forest clearing is small. There are, however, signs of a natural advance of pine in successive stages down from the location of the present state highway into this mounded area, with mounds, buried more or less deeply by woods soil, extending all the way up to the highway.

Each meadow has its peculiar character and its dominating note of interest. Around Whalers Cove and focused in its center is a low terrace meadow surrounded by an upper terrace largely open and also meadow, giving a fine opportunity to see the terraced formation.

In the Pelican Point area one is unpleasantly reminded of the close presence of highway fence, cuts, and traffic, and by the Carmel Highlands subdivision that might easily bring building developments to the hill east of the highway which would dominate this whole end of the "natural" Reserve. Beside these areas are numerous little meadows full of a variety of interest, tucked away all over the Reserve—well worth exploring, from the point of view of the artist, the naturalist, or the less specialized nature lover.

Pine Forest Interiors

THREE DISTINCT TYPES of pine forest areas can be enjoyed within the Reserve. The first of these areas is the kind where the trees are spaced out quite widely, some of them retaining considerable low foliage here and there, and with sufficient light entering to support grass and flowers on the forest floor. Pictorially, this is the outstanding type with its foliage masses contrasting with the ground cover and more distant views, and composing an endless variety of vistas. The pine tree forms are of the most robust and healthy appearance in these areas. The grass and flowers and clumps of rhus, or "poison oak," make these woods always colorful with their seasonal changes.

A second kind of pine forest area is apparently more characteristic of Monterey pine in its most favorable habitat in that, due to crowding, the trees tend to have less vigor and health. This is the character of close, continuous stands of tall, bare-stemmed trees, which are progressively decreasing their spacing through natural crowding. Underbrush is almost entirely limited to occasional live oaks, and in a few places, thickets of young pines where there have been recent openings. Pictorially less interesting than more open and irregular stands, these areas nevertheless have a certain esthetic charm, particularly where the trees are fairly large and wide-spaced, and not too cluttered with spindling, suppressed trees, dying or dead or fallen, and lying criss-cross on the forest floor. The gray shafts of the trees topped by a high crown of foliage, infinite in their variations of size and curve and spacing are in many places saved from the danger of monotony of color by an occasional poison-oak vine hung in lacy reds and greens high up in a gray pine trunk.

Young trees, suppressed trees, old flat-headed veterans, dead and fallen trees, large and small, in normal quantities, all help to complete the presentment of an unbroken life cycle. All this in turn is part of the longer progression of change and evolution that leads up to what one is looking at—Pine Forests, that is—out of the dawn of all trees. And this, again in turn, is part of the even larger picture that includes the mound formations and the old strand terraces skirting the forest margins.

This type of scenery is not peculiar to Point Lobos, and, in fact, is seen at its best in forests of other trees that are larger and more graceful than the Monterey pine. The principal inherent value of the pine forest at Point Lobos is that it gives background to the meadow margins and increases the variety of conditions visible here—conditions that are typical of the coastal shelf. And what will make all this of even greater worth will be unbroken freedom from human interference.

Now we may consider the third type of pine forest effect, which is that found on steep, tree-clad slopes facing north onto Carmel Bay. Here one obtains striking views, out through the tree trunks, over the bay. The value of this effect varies with the density of the forest. If the trees are too thick, the views are obscured, but not so completely that one is not still conscious that the view is there, and consequently one resents the close obscuring trees. Because the trees on these slopes grow tall and leggy they present the appearance of a skeleton forest of the kind that is sometimes left by the more careful lumbering operations. The strongest esthetic effects in these areas depend upon strong contrasts between the foreground pattern of trees and the more distant views. Such effects are best seen on clear, sunny days.

On the floor of this type of pine forest, especially in late spring, mock heather, Indian paintbrush, and in more open areas close to the shore, beds of sea daisies bring strong dashes of color—the three primary colors that contrast sharply with the background greens of the surrounding forest.

One outstanding area of this kind of open forest is to be found in the long tongue of woods separating the north shore meadows from those of the south shore. Another outstanding area is in the smaller, low area just north of the Vierras Knoll plateau. The close-standing type of pine forest is best seen along the highway (or trail) from Rat Hill south. The north-sloping forest area is most typical in the bowl-like slope surrounding Bluefish Cove, although there it is thin and too full of dead and sickly trees to be at its best esthetically. Also, here is [1935] a very heavy new crop of seedlings growing up that is likely not only to smother the outlook but to obscure the rather fine effect of the bowl-like ground form, and this will certainly result in another crop of trees too tall and too weak. On the northeast side of Whalers Knoll is a variation of this type of forest—one of long standing that contains some sizable timber, living and dead, and perhaps representing the least tampered-with piece of pine woods in the Reserve. Here are to be found numerous squirrels and birds busily seeking food and shelter. This area contains some fine panoramic views that are particularly interesting because they look out over and between the cypress-covered and pine-covered knolls along the north shore. Big Dome is a very striking picture when framed by these trees.

With pine forests and cypress forests, with hills and meadows and chaparral, with a sea front of spectacular aspect, Point Lobos Reserve presents indeed a wide variety of types of landscape beauty. Unique in some of its features, it remains typical of the finest reaches of the Central California coast as once it was. Infinitely diverse, rich in color, dramatic in significance, Point Lobos is an abiding inspiration for lovers of the American scene.

1—Sea otter were not seen at Point Lobos during the original Point Lobos Study in 1933. However, in 1938 a group of them was sighted living quietly just eleven miles south. In 1954 they were finally sighted within the Reserve itself. Today the Reserve is a recognized nursery area where mothers with pups are frequently observed.

IV

The Geology of Point Lobos

Ralph W. Chaney/R. A. Bramkamp

Introduction

*A*T POINT LOBOS, *where the forces of surf and weather have for countless centuries battered the edge of the continent, the "record of the rocks" reveals a story of many chapters.*

Rocks on Point Lobos show varied conditions of origin. Granite (grano-diorite), once cooled from a molten mass of rock far below the surface, has been raised up and exposed on Cypress Headland and along much of the northern coast of the Reserve. Fragments worn or broken from it and from other rocks were heaped in layers as sand and gravel along the shore, and have since been cemented into rock which we call sandstone and conglomerate, making up what has been called the Carmelo formation. Occasional fossils found in these sediments indicate that they were laid down and cemented together at a time when this area was beneath the surface of the sea. More recently, as a part of mountain-making which produced the California Coast Ranges, all of this area has been uplifted and the rock formations have been folded and carved by wave, wind, rain and other forces until Point Lobos as we know it today was finally produced.

The geological features of Point Lobos State Reserve that are of special educational value include: 1. The presence of a mass of igneous rock apparently formed at considerable depth and at high temperature, and then slowly cooled to form a granodiorite that contains large crystals of quartz, feldspar and mica; 2. Sedimentary structures of the Carmelo formation that indicate past ocean current and wave conditions similar to those now prevailing along this part of the California coast; 3. The development of old sea-cut terraces considerably above present sea level, but nevertheless similar in form and character to the terrace now being cut along the coast, thus indicating recent changes in sea level; 4. The action of the waves on a coastline composed of various rocks and various structural features.

Point Lobos State Reserve is of exceptional geologic interest for two reasons. First, it includes the most extensive known exposures of the Carmelo formation and is thus the best place to attempt to determine the conditions of origin, age and source of that formation; and second, because of its exposure, wave action is particularly intense, and the shoreline provides an excellent opportunity to study the relations between the ocean and evolving shore forms.

Point Lobos is composed of rocks of four ages, of which the oldest is the Santa Lucia granodiorite. Resting on this is the Carmelo formation which is considered to be of Paleocene age (sixty million years old). The other two units which are of minor importance are the Pleistocene terrace deposits and the modern alluvium and beach deposits.

Ralph W. Chaney, a professor of paleontology at the University of California, has directed field work in Cenozoic paleobotany in western, Central, and South America, as well as in many parts of Asia. He was an early member and long-time director of the Save-the-Redwoods League and was closely associated with the rediscovery of the Dawn redwood in China. He has been a member of the Advisory Board of the National Park Service, and the National Academy of Science, and has written and edited numerous articles in the fields of geology and paleobotany. He has been president of the Save-the-Redwoods League since 1961.

R. A. Bramkamp was a research assistant in paleontology at the University of California at the time the Point Lobos Advisory Committee's report was being compiled. This chapter is based on his detailed field investigation of the geology of Point Lobos as supervised by Professor Chaney.

During and just after storms, the surf at Point Lobos can be extremely violent. The wave in this picture is exploding well over fifty feet up into the exposed granite face of North Point.

Santa Lucia Granodiorite

THE REGION OF Vierras Knoll, Punta de los Lobos Marinos itself, and much of the northern coast of the park are carved from a coarse-grained igneous rock known as Santa Lucia granodiorite. The occurrence of this rock in the region of Carmel Bay is an extension of the much larger occurrence of the same material in the core of the northern part of the Santa Lucia Range. It is granitic in texture, and within the Reserve is marked by many large inclusions of crystalline feldspar, quartz and other materials such as mica. These inclusions are most common in the northern part of the Reserve and tend to share a roughly parallel orientation. This is thought to indicate a certain amount of circulation in the rock prior to solidification. In the southern part of the park the rock is more even-grained and only rarely are the large phenocrysts developed, and then only imperfectly. Dikes and irregular masses of granitic material marked by large crystals of quartz, feldspar, and mica may be seen at various scattered points, especially on Point Lobos proper.

Subsequent to the solidification of the granodiorite, and previous to the deposition of the Carmelo formation, a long period of intensive erosion must have ensued. The coarse grain of the granitic rock indicates slow cooling, and this in turn indicates the existence then of a thick insulating mantle of sedimentary or other rocks. No remnant of this covering remains in the park, and erosion has apparently cut deeply into the igneous rock itself. To the southeast in the Santa Lucia Mountains, large areas of metamorphic rocks (highly altered by the intruding granodiorite) indicate the character of part of this insulating mantle. Though this mantle is thousands of feet thick, it was probably much thicker in the past. Thus we can assume that thousands and perhaps tens of thousands of feet of this mantle must have been removed from Point Lobos and the surrounding area after the solidification of the granodiorite and before the deposition of the Carmelo formation.

The time of the intrusion of the granodiorite cannot be fixed with accuracy. It is clearly younger than the sediments now represented by metamorphic rocks into which it intrudes. In any case, rocks of Cretaceous age (some 110 million years old) are known to rest with depositional contact on it, indicating that the granodiorite is clearly the earlier of the two formations.

Carmelo Formation

THE MOST IMPORTANT formation in the park is a group of sediments, mainly conglomerate, that are known as the Carmelo formation. This formation occurs at other places on the shore of Carmel Bay, but is best developed in the Reserve, especially along the shore south of Punta de los Lobos Marinos, and along the southern shore of Whalers Cove.

Where no disturbing factors intervene, the Carmelo formation seems to rest with depositional contact on an erosional surface cut in the Santa Lucia granodiorite, a contact which may be readily seen in the small cove just north of Headland Cove Beach. Here, as at other localities, there has

Here the Carmelo formation can be seen resting with "depositional contact" on the granite—evidence that the granite is older than the conglomerate Carmelo formation.

been considerable faulting and shearing of both the Carmelo formation and the granodiorite, but on the north side of the cove the contact seems to be depositional. The surface beneath the Carmelo formation is strikingly irregular, showing a relief of at least six feet along the seventy-five feet of the contact which is exposed there. Several slabs of granodiorite ranging up to three feet in length occur in the sediments immediately above the contact, and as will be mentioned later the matrix of the conglomerate is of such a nature that it could have been derived from the underlying granodiorite.

The exact thickness of the Carmelo formation cannot be determined accurately because of the faults of unknown displacement, or of the smaller, more numerous shear planes whose extent cannot be evaluated. The least disturbed section occurs between the point near Seal Rocks and a point on the sea-cliff about 1800 feet to the northeast. If small shear planes and minor faults are disregarded, the Carmelo formation appears to be 750 to 1300 feet thick.

The Carmelo formation is made up of a series of conglomerates intermixed with varying amounts of sand and sandy shale. In fresh exposures, which are uncommon, the sandstones and conglomerates are gray in color, but in the normal exposures the conglomerate is usually dark brown and the sandstone buff-colored. Except where they are exceptionally badly weathered, the shales tend to be nearly black. In the lower parts of the conglomerate section there is relatively little sandstone, but in the upper levels it may equal the conglomerate in volume. The lower sandstones occur as lenticular beds—six- to eight-foot-thick layers that invariably taper down and disappear within a short distance either by thinning out or by the gradual addition of pebbles until they become indistinguishable from the conglomerate. In the upper parts of the Carmelo formation the sandstone beds are much thicker, and zones reaching forty feet have been seen. Sandy shales of a characteristic black color are present sporadically in the sandstones, usually in zones several inches thick in which layers of shale alternate with beds of sandstone. At three localities, one on the southeastern shore of Carmel Cove, and the others at the two ends of Gibson Creek Beach, masses of shale with interbedded sandstone are present. Faulting makes it impossible to place these shales stratigraphically but it is probable that they belong relatively high in the Carmelo formation.

The conglomerate of the Carmelo formation consists of a moderately well-hardened rock, the individual pebbles or rocks ranging from one to five inches in diameter imbedded in a matrix of finer material. Some few of the pebbles exceed five inches but these are uncommon. As a general rule the pebbles are well rounded and smooth, usually having a sub-spherical or sub-ellipsoidal form. They show a remarkable uniformity of composition and eighty to ninety percent of the material is composed of fine-grained, porphyritic igneous rocks which range in composition from rhyolite to dacite and may include some rather acid andesite. All of these pebbles have a fine-grained, dense ground-mass and are of a type capable of withstanding considerable mechanical abrasion. The remainder of the pebbles includes fragments of shale, fragments of the underlying Santa Lucia granodiorite, and occasionally some vitreous quartzites and red cherts, the latter often showing white veins of silica.

The matrix of the conglomerate differs markedly in composition from the pebbles and is composed principally of poorly rounded grains of quartz and feldspar with some mica. The latter may be much altered, sometimes to chlorite, but often is comparatively fresh. The feldspar when unaffected by recent weathering is commonly fresh and glassy. The cement of the conglomerate is mainly clayey and reddish, iron-bearing material, though some calcium carbonate is also present.

The highly varied position of the layers and other structural elements may be taken as an indication that ocean currents of variable intensity and direction were important in the deposition of the Carmelo formation, and also that many of these currents were relatively strong. Perhaps the most suitable place for such conditions of erosion and deposition within a limited area is in the immediate vicinity of a shore-

Eroded sandstone layers in the foreground sweep up to an old marine terrace that is being undercut by present-day wave action.

line with relatively strong wave action. In addition to the variations in currents produced by the waves themselves in such a situation, there may be conflicting currents dependent on direction of wind, character of the shoreline, tides and other factors.

Marine fossils occur in the Carmelo formation in calcareous sandstones near the center of Gibson Creek Beach. A number of unidentified mollusks (all of which seem to be marine) were found along with a marine snail, *Turritella*. Though in a rather poor state of preservation it is apparently a variant of *Turritella pacheoensis* Stanton. If this determination is correct, it implies that the Carmelo formation belongs to the Martinez (Paleocene, or Lower Eocene) age. Moreover, the presence of these marine fossils indicates that the Carmelo formation is of marine origin in some part, and that the entire Carmelo formation was laid down near the strand line of the sea of that time.

Fragments of vegetable material were also found in the Carmelo formation, though these have not been identified and are so poor in quality that it may not be possible to tell much about them. In any case, a relatively large amount of plant material did reach the site of deposition of the Carmelo formation, a fact which suggests that there was a considerable plant life cover with woody types of stems on the adjacent highlands.

The sandy matrix of the conglomerates, the sandstones, and the coarser grains of the shales have presumably been derived from rocks the same or similar in composition to the granodiorite beneath the Carmelo formation, and probably have been transported only short distances. A similar source may be suggested for the granitic and quartz or feldspar pebbles of the conglomerate. These pebbles and grains do not show the effects of long-continued abrasion, nor are they capable of withstanding much abrasion.

Most of the pebbles of the conglomerate cannot have had such a simple history. Their high degree of rounding in combination with their resistant character indicates long-continued abrasion. Thus their presence in the Carmelo formation, which otherwise has had an essentially local source, is anomalous. Similar pebbles have been found in sediments of various ages in many parts of the Coast Ranges of California, but their original source is as yet undetermined.

The most likely explanation, however, is that the pebbles have been reworked from a Cretaceous conglomerate somewhere in the near vicinity. Cretaceous beds which could be a source for such pebbles exist ten or fifteen miles south of Point Lobos. The Cretaceous is also well developed north of Monterey Bay, although it is not known whether conglomerates of similar character are present there. Certainly Cretaceous deposits were more widespread in the vicinity of Carmel Bay at the time of deposition of the Carmelo formation than they are at present, although it cannot be demonstrated with certainty that they were in a proper position to furnish debris to the Carmelo formation.

SUMMARY: *The following facts concerning the Carmelo formation seem to be indicated.*
1. *The Carmelo formation was probably deposited under conditions of strong and variable currents and wave action at or near the coastline of that time.*

2. *The Carmelo formation is probably of Paleocene age, as indicated by a small fauna of marine invertebrates.*
3. *Abundant carbonaceous matter at a number of localities suggests that a considerable mantle of vegetation was present on adjacent coastal highlands.*
4. *The sediments of the Carmelo formation were probably derived in part from the erosion of granitic rocks in the immediate area. To this was added material which may have been reworked from Cretaceous conglomerates which were probably not far distant.*

Present conditions at Point Lobos as compared with those considered probable for the Carmelo formation seem to indicate that the coast is rising, or has risen recently, with reference to sea level, so that sediments near the shoreline are not now accumulating. During Carmelo time a sinking coastline permitted the accumulation of the considerable thickness of Carmelo sediments near the shore, instead of the material being disintegrated and carried out to the edge of the continental shelf, as is the case at the present time.

Terraces

THE MAIN UPLAND SURFACE of Point Lobos State Reserve, back from the seacliffs, is composed of a combination of three marine terraces and their inter-terrace slopes. Terraces have been found up to an elevation of 800 feet in the region of Carmel Bay, and even higher terraces have been reported along the coast of central California. The highest represented in the park has an elevation of about 215 feet above sea level, and this is only imperfectly preserved. It may be seen near the summit of Whalers Knoll and is well developed in a few places to the southeast of the park. The summit of Big Dome may also be a remnant of this terrace. At lower levels, later marine erosion has cut deeply into the terrace leaving only the few remnants mentioned so that little can be said of the original form and character. Deposits have not been found on this terrace.

The next lower terrace has an elevation of about 125 feet at its landward edge. Intermediate, less well developed terraces may be present between this and the higher terrace, but they are obscure and cannot be traced. The 125-foot terrace has a moderate seaward slope, and where it is wide its outer edge may be within seventy-five feet of sea level. It covers the main and central part of the park, extending out onto Point Lobos. The shoreline followed approximately the course of the old state highway, with the exception of a promontory at Rat Hill. The slopes above the edge of the terrace are now relatively gentle and presumably are the result of the seacliffs being modified by subsequent sub-serial erosion. Except for some slightly steepened places, nothing is left of the cliffs which must have been present. The terrace surface is gently undulating, presumably due to irregularities in the original wave-cut shelf. Sands and gravel are present as terrace deposits, but these seldom exceed a thickness of six or eight feet. The low ridge that now connects Rat Hill and Whalers Knoll must once have been a gently rounded, rocky shoal very possibly exposed at exceptionally low tides. Whalers Knoll, Big Dome, and a small part of the summit of Point

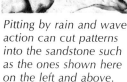
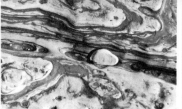

Pitting by rain and wave action can cut patterns into the sandstone such as the ones shown here on the left and above.

Intricate designs are revealed by exposure of iron stains in the sandstone. Patterns such as the one on the right are the result of "ironstone" ridges standing slightly above the surrounding sandstone matrix.

Lobos were probably islands. At the time this terrace was being cut, sea level apparently remained constant for a considerable period of time because extensive marine erosion was able to remove much of the higher terrace.

A third halt in the retreat of the sea is represented by a low-level terrace which has an elevation of thirty-five to forty feet. Well developed sections of this terrace have been found in the Point Sur area. It is much less extensive than the next higher terrace, and clearly represents a shorter period of stable relations between land and sea levels. This terrace is well developed intermittently along the north and west shores of the Reserve, especially where relatively soft rocks have permitted the waves to erode more deeply into the land. The slopes above its strand line are steeper than those above the 125-foot terrace, and while actual cliffs have not been preserved, it is apparent that the amount of erosion necessary to reduce them to their present form is not great. The surface of the terrace, like the next higher one, has a gentle seaward slope. At some localities, especially in the meadow east of Pebbly Beach, a series of low hummocks up to two feet in height are developed. These are spaced about thirty to forty feet apart over most of the surface of the meadow. This area is poorly drained because a very fine textured, impervious, sandy clay soil lies immediately beneath the surface. It lies just below the lower spots and continues at about the same level throughout the entire meadow area though it is more deeply buried beneath the surface soil of the mounds or hummocks. (Similar hummocks have also been reported on the next higher terrace.)

At present much of the surface of the park is covered with a black soil mantle which is generally three or four feet in thickness. Shells of abalone and other edible mollusks are common in the soil at a number of places and presumably represent Indian kitchen-middens. Such shells may also be seen in the soil of Bird Rock though this island is now separated from the mainland by a deep channel.

Modern Erosion

POINT LOBOS clearly illustrates the relation between character of rocks, intensity and direction of wave action, and the resultant form of the coastline. Wave action, especially during or just after storms, is particularly intense here because of the Point's exposed position. Strong undercutting by the waves in combination with vertical jointing and the attitude of the sedimentary formations have served to produce cliffs of varying height around much of the shore of the Reserve. Granodiorite which is relatively resistant to the attack of the waves, makes up Point Lobos proper and the promontories near Bird Island. Seal Rocks, however, indicate that the conglomerate, when massive, is nearly as resistant. The interbedded sandstones and conglomerates around Whalers Cove and Pebbly Beach have proved less resistant, resulting in indentations in the coastline. In those areas where the Carmelo formation lies at an angle to the present coastline, narrow inlets have been formed in the more easily eroded sandstone beds, while the conglomerate areas have formed small promontories.

A secondary feature of the coastline is the relation between the direction and nature of shear which the rocks have suffered, and the jointing which is represented. This is best observed in the relatively homogeneous granitic rocks of Punta de los Lobos Marinos where several deep inlets can be seen to follow zones of weakness resulting from a single series of parallel shear planes, or sometimes by a combination of two or more systems. Similar features have also resulted from weakening of the conglomerates by shear, although on a lesser scale. In one case on the Point near Seal Rocks the waves penetrate at least 150 feet inland along a crack hardly ten feet wide at its widest point. During times of heavy surf tremendous pressures are developed at the end of these cavities and in those places where the cliffs are undercut. Water may be thrown back or high into the air, and erosion is obviously rapid at such points.

The sand and gravel on the various beaches can be readily correlated with the rock type that is supplying debris to that particular locality. In inlets like China Beach where only granitic rocks are exposed the beach is covered with extremely fine-grained sand. The granodiorite tends to disintegrate along the boundaries of its component mineral crystals rather than breaking into larger fragments. In those areas where wave action is particularly severe, however, preliminary disintegration is less perfect, and boulders are found. In areas where wave action is at work on Carmelo formation conglomerates, the finer matrix material tends to be quickly washed away, leaving just the pebbles on nearby beaches.

On the rounded hill just south of Headland Cove, wind action has been involved to a minor extent. Two prevailing wind directions seem to be indicated. One from the southwest has served to carry sand from the beaches up over the headland. Depressions along the northeast edge of this hill indicate that the second prevailing set of wind from the northwest has been an erosional as well as a transportational agency.

*Their ghostly trunks and branches twisted by the wind, their roots exposed by soil erosion,
these individual cypress trees still cling to life, and their kind continues on the earth.*

V

A 'Tree Island' of Monterey Cypress

Willis Linn Jepson

Willis Linn Jepson, a world-renowned professor of botany at the University of California, Berkeley, was one of the founders of the Save-the-Redwoods League, and served as an advisor to the League from 1920 until his death in 1946. His work carried him throughout the remote mountain and desert sections of California, and to Syria, Palestine, Alaska, and the Bering Sea as well. He was an editor and frequent contributor to professional journals on botany, and author of *The Silva of California, An Illustrated Manual of the Flowering Plants of California,* and other books. Part of this chapter originally appeared in the Sierra Club Bulletin for February 1933. The balance of the chapter is based on a portion of his book *The Silva of California.*

TWO ROCKY HEADLANDS, Point Lobos and Cypress Point, one on either side, mark the mouth of the Carmel River, which empties into the Pacific Ocean a few miles south of Monterey Bay. These headlands are small, so small as to border on the insignificant save for this, that each of them bears a narrow forest of a remarkable sort, consisting solely of one kind of cypress tree, and they have thus become endowed with a unique and singular interest. In the way of botanical observers, the trees were first seen in 1786 by Jean François Galoup de la Perouse, commander of an ill-fated scientific expedition from France that, two years later, was lost in the South Seas. Since that early day many other expeditions to the California coast have come and gone, and we now know definitely, after this long period of searching, that the Monterey cypress (*Cupressus macro-carpa*) does not occur naturally at any other locality in California—nor elsewhere in the world.

The trees grow on the summits of the headlands and on the very face of the cliffs within reach of flying salt spray from the ocean. So exposed are they that the power of the sea may occasionally undermine an individual on the steep face of the rocks, and the tree falls into the thundering gulf below. The Cypress Point grove on the north headland is the larger—a half-mile long, in breadth measuring 300 yards at its widest. The Point Lobos grove lies on a higher and wider headland to the south. On both headlands the trees of the cliffs and shore-line carry in their architecture and in their outline, often boldly proclaimed against the sky, the life story of their battle with centuries of storm and wind from the Pacific Ocean—a battle which has been recorded in the structural details of the tree's organs—an intense struggle to maintain one last foothold on the Californian shore. The thick weave of the clustered masses of the foliage, as smooth as a lawn on the seaward side, the long, gaunt arms, weirdly irregular and picturesque, the vertical structural bracing of the boardlike trunks and main branches—all these things typify combat, resistance, long-enduring tenacity.

While no two trees of the storm-driven type are alike, all give out so powerful and dramatic a picture as to make deep appeal to the poet, the lay traveler, the mystically minded. For now [1933] three generations, a river of people who come to see, have flowed past the Carmel shores. Frankly exclamatory, or murmuring low one to the other, or querulously skeptical as the eyes turn from an angular wind driven cypress to another cypress quite near at hand, that has grown full and straight with all the beauty of perfect symmetry—all emotions have centered in questionings. Whence came these trees? How is it that they are found only here in California? Why should they have such strange and at times peculiar shapes? In answer to these and many other queries there has grown up a large body of folk-legend as odd and as curious as the trees themselves. Some of the folk-stories insist that the Monterey cypress is the same as the Lebanon cedar of the Lebanon Mountains of Syria (a statement innocent of the botanical fact that the Lebanon cedar belongs to the Pine family and that the Monterey cypress is of the Cypress family); that the tree came by the hand of pious pilgrims from the Holy Land as a sign to the devout; that it was brought across the Pacific Ocean from Japan many centuries ago and planted here by Buddhist monks; and so on in many tones and variations.

Nevertheless, the tree has a real history, the beginnings of which are slowly being unfolded as a result of research on the geological history of the California coast and the study of ancient plant migrations. During recent geological periods the eastern part of the North American continent has been relatively stable, but during the same time the coast of California has passed through successive periods of very impressive uplift and correspondingly great subsidence. For a long time it has been a theory of this writer that during the Pleistocene epoch an extensive forest filled the south Coast Range country including the land that then united the Santa Barbara Islands with the mainland. The changes which have occurred since, in connection with climatic cycles, are thus made to account for the restriction or localization of many of the forest trees that once composed that ancient forest.

The Monterey pine (*Pinus radiata*) occurs in a few small areas along the coast—small sharply defined areas in which this species is dominant, and which, hence, are ecologically termed "islands." The Bishop pine (*Pinus muricata*) is also found only along the seacoast and often in narrow "islands," especially southward. The Catalina ironwood (*Lyonothamnus floribundus*) is now restricted to three of the islands of the Santa Barbara group. The Torrey pine (*Pinus torreyana*) is another highly localized species, limited to a small area on the San Diego coast and to the south end of Santa Rosa Island. The Santa Lucia fir (*Abies venusta*) grows only in the Santa Lucia Mountains. The Gowen cypress (*Cupressus goveniana*) is a dwarf growing in a few tiny areas near Monterey. As our knowledge of past time increases, we are learning that the coastal species of our native trees once had a much greater range. Well-borers on the coastal plain at Los Angeles have brought up fragments of redwood, thus extending a long distance southward the present time-range of that species. In the asphalt beds at Carpinteria far to the south of the present mainland range of Monterey pine, Ralph W. Chaney and Herbert L. Mason have uncovered excellently well preserved specimens of Monterey pine cones. Long ago this writer identified Monterey pine cones taken from the strata at Bodega Head and at Mussel Rock far to the north of the present Monterey pine range.

It is increasingly evident that we are only at the beginning of this unfolding history, and we may confidently say that the Monterey cypress is a relic of the Pleistocene, a reminder of a silva which has been subject to a long series of migrations following upon the succession of profound geological changes that finally made the California coast what it is today. Indeed, the Monterey cypress, clinging to the edge of the continental shelf, is, as a species, the most dramatic witness of past changes on the western shore line. It has seen the Santa Lucia Mountains take on their present form, with knife-like canyons cutting direct to the sea; it has seen the Coast Range foothills soften and smooth to their present velvet-flowing slopes; it has seen many forest species migrate from the mountain tops to the shore line to avoid extinction; it has seen the "Golden Gate," that is the one main outlet to the ocean for waters from the Great Valley, move from Monterey Bay to San Francisco Bay. All in all a fine pageant to have witnessed.

No other tree, from this consideration, is so deserving of the protection which can be afforded by enclosure within the limits of a park sanctuary. Its singular beauty lends a special charm to this bit of coast. No other tree on earth has so narrow a natural range, though when its full history is finally written, it is likely that this cypress will show a range as long as California, or possibly much longer. It has today a wider horticultural distribution over the earth than any other California tree species; and yet it cannot or does not extend back naturally, that is to say, spontaneously, from the shore line over land which is now and has been barren of trees. Interesting and pregnant questions multiply constantly about it. All thought, all contemplation, all study are here in a sufficient way eminently worth the mind's attention. It is one tree whose full history will be highly enlightening, and it will in time easily take its place among the most well-known trees of the earth's silva.

Scientific Notes on the Monterey Cypress
An abridged extract from *The Silva of California*, by Willis L. Jepson

Cupressus macrocarpa Hartweg (Monterey cypress). Littoral tree, fifteen to eighty feet high with trunk one to three feet in diameter, the branches spreading and forming a regular conical crown or exceedingly distorted and irregular; ultimate branchlets numerous, fine and subterate, densely clothed with triangular scale-like leaves; leaves $1/2$ to $1\frac{1}{2}$ inches long; staminate catkins ovate or subglobose, two to four m.m. long, borne at the ends of the ultimate branchlets; ovulate catkins greenish, composed of about five pairs of broadly ovate thinnish scales; cones dull brown, broadly oblong or subglobose, one to $1\frac{3}{4}$ inches long; scales flat-topped, with a central curved thin-edged ridge-like umbo; seeds two to four m.m. long, narrowly wing-margined but irregularly shaped from crowding in the cones and with a minute, white, lanceolate attachment scar at base.

The Monterey cypress inhabits the ocean shore and forms two groves, one at Cypress Point near Monterey and the second at Point Lobos. It is the most restricted in distribution of any California tree and of any coniferous species in the world. The wind-broken and most admired individuals stand in exposed places on the bluffs or cling to the very face of the rocky cliffs within reach of the flying ocean spray. In such situations they are carved into picturesque and oft-times singular shapes remarkable for the density of the masses of foliage presented toward the ocean and the flattened or board-like character of the supporting trunks. A little back from the shore, where the trees protect each other, they assume forms as regular as those of trees in cultivated plantations. Most of these protected trees have very open crowns and finger-pointed main branches.

The effect of the wind upon the trees growing in exposed situations is due more to mechanical strain than excessive

The Old Veteran. The cliff below and the hill above this tree were eroding rapidly in 1905. Now, with soil erosion slowed by increased plant cover, the tree, though broken by the wind, is still alive and apparently thriving.

transpiration because of the moist habitat. One may see two trees standing side by side, of equal height and equally exposed, one a young tree with slender, pointed, symmetrically pyramidal crown, the other an old tree, its trunk shorn of branches and rising to a battered but thick flat-topped crown.

Unsymmetrical trees, whose configuration is due in the main to wind, fall roughly into three types:

1. Trees possessing much thickened lower branches and irregular crowns. 2. Trunks, mainly dismantled of branches, ending above in a flat hat-like crown of compactly woven branchlets. 3. Trees crouching together in small companies and building up to leeward an even, dense wall of foliage.

As a result of wind strain on top, or load of one-sided crown, trunks often become heavily buttressed or swollen unsymmetrically at base. Excessively buttressed trees usually stand in the most exposed places. On the other hand, some trees standing equally near the shore line do not develop

Standing astride a granite ridge this full-topped cypress awaits a coming storm.

buttresses. Buttressing seems to be more or less correlated with root development.

In cultivation the Monterey cypress has long been a favorite shelter and hedge plant in California and is easily propagated by seed which is readily germinated within two or three weeks in open-air nursery beds. Each cone produces about 150 seeds. The seedlings grow with weed-like rapidity. Practically all cypress hedges in California are of this species. It lends itself to the art of formal gardening, and is almost always clipped into regular or even fantastic shapes. It is a successful windbreak and is much used for that purpose since it will grow an erect body in places where the wind promptly controls other species. It has also been widely planted as an ornamental tree, but has comparatively little to recommend it save its rapid growth and dense crown.

The present exceedingly limited area of its natural home must have been caused by change in climatic conditions, since the tree itself is vigorous and readily adapts itself to cultivation in many parts of the world. Its seeds are light and easily dispersed; they germinate promptly under favorable conditions; the seedlings grow rapidly and show vigor. Nevertheless this species could never extend itself over the dry Coast Range hills unaided. Grown in the interior their constitutional vigor seems weakened by the dryness of the hot valleys and they succumb to the attacks of borers.

The age of Monterey cypress in the native groves is not readily determinable since the trees, on account of their rarity and interest, are not cut either for fuel or lumber. One fallen tree sawn through to remove it from a roadway was ninety-eight years old and had a trunk two feet in diameter. Since the tree grows rapidly it would seem fair to hazard the opinion that 200 to 300 years represent the extreme age of the older trees. The advertisement of them in seaside literature as 1,000 to 2,000 years old does not, as far as the writer is able to determine, rest upon any actual data, and probably represents a desire to minister to a popular craving for superlatives.

Hartweg found *Cupressus macrocarpa* near Carmel in 1846 and on his specimens the species was founded. Seed, however, was collected at an earlier date and sent to England, the seedling trees being called *Cupressus lambertiana*. Since 1840 or so the Monterey cypress has been planted in England and various parts of Europe, and has also been carried to Australia and southern South America. In New Zealand it is widely planted as a shelter plant, but as in California, it is short-lived except on deep soil near the coast.

In horticulture a number of color, leaf and branch forms have been developed; in one (var. *lutes*) the tips of the branches are light yellow or golden, changing to green in the second year; in another (var. *Crippsii*) the leaves are spreading instead of appressed with the tips of the youngest growth light yellow; in a third (var. *lambertiana*) the habit is spreading. The var. *farallonensis* Masters is perhaps a cultural form whose origin is unknown. It certainly could not have been derived from the barren, rocky Farallon Islands, as stated by Dr. Masters.

The wood is heavy, hard, strong, and close-grained, the basal parts of the trunks in particular furnishing highly ornamental patterns.

Silhouetted by the fading light of a westering sun,
these dead cypress trees are eloquent symbols
of tenacity and perseverance.

VI

A Pageant of Flowering Plants

Herbert L. Mason

Herbert L. Mason was a professor of botany and for many years curator of the herbarium at the University of California, Berkeley. His primary field of interest was botany, paleobotany, and the natural evolution of plant forms. This chapter is based on his findings as a member of the Point Lobos Advisory Committee.

T REES, SHRUBS, AND WILD FLOWERS at Point Lobos were given "a new lease on life," when a policy was adopted by its guardians, the essence of which is to interfere as little as possible with natural processes. Protective measures have been taken, but they are not obtrusive. The result has been that there is freshness and naturalness in even the least spectacular portions of the Reserve, and from this feature many visitors derive great enjoyment.

At almost any season of the year, everywhere at Point Lobos, there is color. Gold of California poppies, yellow of buttercups, creamcups, Brodiaeas, azure of the sky and sea brought to earth by blue lupine and Ceanothus, reds of the Indian paintbrush, greens of the shrubs and ferns, made darker and richer by the background of cypress leaning against the sky, and pines across the grassy meadows—these are splashes of color that continually change.

In spring, color is also splashed about with the pink of the rose, the lavender and white of the shooting star and, though it is more rare, the Dodecatheon, a plant that is related to the primrose and sometimes called cyclamen or mad violet. There are gay Johnny-jump-ups —often called yellow or "wild" violets. Besides creamcups and tidytips, and purple Brodiaeas, there are rose mallow and filaree. Hung over cliff's edge are fringes of native grass and sea daisies rippling in the wind.

Some of the desert-like exposed parts of the point are painted yellow by lupine. This hardy member of the pea family thrives well roundabout Carmel, growing high at times— fragrant with the yellow or the blue flowers. There are annual, biennial and perennial varieties. The bush lupine, which needs abundant sunshine, grows in sandy spots. Blue-flowered ground lupine is also present though it is less plentiful than other varieties.

As a "plant refuge" Point Lobos Reserve performs an important function in giving complete protection to one species of great significance to California. For this species, the official state flower, has retreated considerably from its original natural range. The Spanish called it *Copa de oro* or "cup of gold," but the botanist has named it Eschscholtzia californica, and popularly it is called the golden poppy. The scientific name of the poppy was acquired when a Russian scientific expedition under Kotzebue, in 1815, explored the California coastland. Chamisso, naturalist with the expedition, named the species for Dr. Eschscholtz, a companion naturalist.

As one wanders the trails of Point Lobos in spring, one is likely to think that no state has

The mood of Point Lobos changes with the season, the weather, the time of day.
It can be joyous and festive, or stormy and violent. Or, as in this photograph, it can be
profoundly quiet and gentle—the motionless sea merging with the sky beyond a thin veil of haze.

chosen its representative flower more appropriately than California. The gold of this poppy seems to have the very essence of California sunshine woven into its brightness. During the spring it covers field and mountainside with a cloth of gold. In the past, when it was more prevalent, men and women and children made a festival of gathering the poppy, as the Japanese do with their cherry blossoms. And tradition has it that many a vast field of these poppies used to serve as a landmark, almost as a beacon, to coasting ships offshore; that in old Spanish times the coast often was called The Land of Fire, and that on occasion thanks were given "to sacred San Pascual who had spread a golden altar-cloth upon the hills."

Including trees and shrubs, close to six hundred species of flowering plants have been counted on the varied terrain of Point Lobos. There are other growing things too, such as the marine algae, or seaweeds, and lichens and mosses, all of which have interest for botanists.

To many people, however, the main impression in most of the months is that a great wealth of bloom, in color masses, adds embellishment to the striking vistas of sea and headland.

Point Lobos is notable not only for the number of separate species found here, but also for the unusual variety of groups or associations of plants found within a small area.

These are the general divisions of the flora of the Reserve: (1) The cypress groves of the headlands along Carmel Bay, (2) the pine forests of the areas back from the ocean, (3) the meadow flora, (4) the sea-bluff flora, (5) the sandhills flora, (6) the ruderal flora, on the formerly tilled lands, (7) a soft chaparral flora on the northwest face of Whalers Knoll and in the quarry back of Whalers Cove, (8) the marine flora in the surf. Many of the Pacific Coast seaweeds were first discovered in the vicinity of Point Lobos, making this region the type locality for these species and the source of authentic material for the future.

The more one explores Point Lobos, the more one dis-covers about the Point's varied plant life—forms both beautiful and curious. The "rock gardens" along the inaccessible bluffs above the surf are teeming with succulents tinted in pastel shades of green and buff and rose. The mosses and lichens are features of great interest to many. The almost weird "atmosphere" on portions of Cypress Headland can be in part attributed to lichens, which are rather conspicuous elements of the vegetation.

Both the Monterey cypress and the Monterey pine are often heavily festooned with a light gray-green "moss." This is not Spanish moss such as is found in the Southeastern United States. Spanish moss has flowers, and belongs to the pineapple family, so the botanists tell us. The "moss" at Point Lobos does not flower, and is actually lace-lichen, the combination of a fungus and an alga living harmoniously together in a single plant structure supported by but not harming the trees upon which they grow. If you look closely you will see that it is made up of lacy nets with meshes from pinpoint fineness to the size of a pencil when full grown. In exposed locations near the sea this lace lichen is matted by the winds, frequently torn and shredded. Yet back in the sheltered pine groves of the Reserve, better specimens are found. Here the lace is luxuriant, hanging from the branches like the folds of a Spanish lace shawl; near the ranger's cottage and on out toward the Point it hangs somberly and drifts slowly in the breeze.

There is another lichen abundant at the Point—the kind that is seen on dead twigs and on rocks. It spreads out in all directions, forming a fuzzy-looking brush, dull olive green to nearly black. Old weathered rocks often owe their color more to lichen than to the rock minerals themselves.

The trees overlooking the bay have their lower branches covered with a growth of red algae. However, we are assured by scientists that this does no damage, since it appears only on dead twigs and on the bark of the living branches and not on the green leaves. But this alga does add color and so contributes interest and beauty to the groves.

In all seasons the landscape is highlighted by a wonderful variety of flowering plants and shrubs.

*Above the broken granite, sunlight shines in the weathered creases
of the cypress stump, and succulent bluff-lettuce brings a flow
of new life cascading over the old.*

VII

Animals: Land & Marine

Joseph Grinnell / Jean M. Linsdale

Joseph Grinnell was a professor of zoology and director of the Museum of Vertebrate Zoology at the University of California, Berkeley. For many years he also served as editor of *The Condor*, the official publication of the Cooper Ornithological Society. He was the author of numerous articles about the distribution and ecology of birds and mammals of California and Alaska. Material used in this chapter was taken from the Grinnell-Linsdale report on the vertebrates of Point Lobos. The report was originally included in the Point Lobos Advisory Committee's study, and was later published separately by the Carnegie Institution of Washington.

Jean M. Linsdale, a research associate in the California Museum of Vertebrate Zoology at the University of California, collaborated with Joseph Grinnell on this and many other studies and reports about the birds and mammals of California.

*I*S THERE MUCH WILDLIFE AT POINT LOBOS? asks the visitor as he considers the comparatively small area in the Reserve.[1] The answer is a definite affirmative. During one year, Dr. Joseph Grinnell and Dr. Jean M. Linsdale observed the presence here of 176 kinds of vertebrate animals—ten amphibians and reptiles, nineteen mammals and 147 birds. Both as regards species and individuals, the count was high in Point Lobos Reserve. They ascribed this partly to the number and diversity of habitats represented, including forests, brushland, grassland, ocean shore and islands.

Next to the spectacular beauty of the Point, this presence of wildlife is among the area's most arresting features. Here it is possible to observe in a primitive environment many plant and animal species living in interesting relationship to each other.

Nearly every plant or animal seen at Point Lobos, with but few exceptions, may be seen in abundance by most Californians at some locality more conveniently accessible than here; but in few places can they be freely examined and studied under undisturbed natural conditions such as are maintained at this Reserve. For example, most visitors to this area are no doubt only slightly interested in white-crowned sparrows themselves, for these are common backyard birds, but here this species of bird can be seen in relation to its natural environment.

Nor has the program followed here been to preserve permanently any specific objects now occurring in the park, but primarily to insure freedom for all the natural processes which have produced those objects and which if permitted to continue will, it is believed, tend to maintain them for a long time in their most valuable form.

Of those natural habitats which attract a wide variety of animals to the Reserve, grassland makes up a larger portion than any other. Several predatory species normally range here, where their prospects of finding suitable prey are greater because of the virtual absence of obstructing vegetation. This in turn requires that animals which live in this low vegetation be so colored as to avoid easy detection or that they have access to burrows into which they may escape. Such a habitat encourages the exercise of acuteness in the senses of sight and hearing, and of alertness in starting to escape when danger threatens.

Seeds, roots and insects constitute a food supply for a few mammals, such as gophers, mice and ground squirrels. Dr. Grinnell and Dr. Linsdale estimated that mammal workings are extensive enough in a year's time to disturb every bit of the surface of the soil of all the grassland to a depth of close to one inch. Presence of seeds and insects, and freedom of movement or vision, attract several kinds of birds which are so closely dependent upon these conditions that they come only as long as the conditions prevail.

Conditions in the brushland favor the animals with restricted power of escape from pursuit and the ones which are accustomed to capture prey by making short dashes. Lupine

California sea otters — quick, curious, intelligent, and playful — are a highlight of the Point Lobos wildlife spectacle.

and Ceanothus particularly provide shade, screen and food for many species.

The trees of the forest—oak, Monterey pine, cypress—accommodate animals usually associated with trees of some sort. As has been emphasized, the presence of the Monterey cypress is responsible, more than any other single circumstance, for the selection and maintenance of Point Lobos as a state reserve. It is somewhat of a surprise to find that few species of vertebrates are satisfied with the cypresses for living quarters. The extremely dense foliage of the trees and the heavy tangle of branches present an almost solid wall which few animals care to penetrate. Under the trees, juncos (the year round), linnets and thrushes (in the winter) are accustomed to forage; winter wrens forage in the very densest branch-work. A few other species feed among the more open portions of the tree tops. Of these the only one that shows preference for the cypresses over the pines is the Townsend warbler. Wood rats commonly build nests among fallen cypress limbs.

The ocean shore is the forage ground and nesting site of numbers of birds, as discussed in the following chapter. The second largest group of islands, known as Seal Rocks, is the hauling-out place for a large herd of Steller and California sea lions. The factors of safety and conveniently available food seem to account for the presence of these animals.

Weather conditions vary markedly, also. A slight slope toward the morning or afternoon sun greatly increases the warmth of certain strips of land. Added to this, the various rises and knolls are effective in deflecting the course of the wind so as to produce many types of climate locally within this comparatively small area.

Mammals Found in Point Lobos Reserve

Mole—*Scapanus latimanus*
California Bat—*Myotis californicus*
Brown Bat—*Eptesicus fuscus*
Ground Squirrel—*Citellus beecheyi*
Gray Squirrel—*Sciurus griseus*
Pocket Gopher—*Thomomys bottae*
Pocket Mouse—*Perognathus californicus*
Harvest Mouse—*Reithrodontomys megalotis*
White-footed Mouse—*Peromyscus maniculatus*
Wood Rat—*Neotoma fuscipes*
Meadow Mouse—*Microtus californicus*
House Mouse—*Mus musculus*
Jack Rabbit—*Lepus californicus* (now rare)
Brush Rabbit—*Sylvilagus bachmani*
Black-tailed Deer—*Odocoileus columbianus*
Oppossum—*Didelphis marsupialis*
Raccoon—*Procyon lotor*
Long-tailed Weasel—*Mustela frenata*
Striped Skunk—*Mephitis mephitis*
Wildcat—*Lynx rufus*
Gray Fox—*Uroeyon cinercorgenteus*
Sea Otter—*Enhydra lutris*
California Sea Lion—*Zalophus californianus*
Steller Sea Lion—*Eumetopias jubata*
Elephant Seal—*Mirounga angustirostris*
Harbor Seal—*Phoca vitulina*
Gray Whale—*Eschrichtius gibbosus*
Killer Whale—*Orcinus orca*

Steller Sea Lion and California Sea Lion

Of all the mammals at Point Lobos the Steller sea lion attracts more attention from visitors than any other. Not only is it the predominant species on the rocks off the shore near the tip of the point, but groups of individuals are seen frequently in the water close to shore. The animals are present the year round, but their numbers seem to increase considerably in the spring, about the middle of April.

Sea lions may be distinguished easily from seals by the presence of an external ear, by their much longer necks, allowing them to carry their heads high, and by their active, sportive and noisy natures. Seals are clumsy, short-necked, quiet animals.

The fur seal, not seen on this coast, is also a sea lion but has a thick under-fur not found on other species. Some writers claim that sea lions received their name because of the lion-like appearance of the faces of some of the huge males. Others say it is the fur manes of the animals which suggested their names.

Not so large as the Steller sea lion, and far more intelligent than a seal, the California sea lion is the one you may have seen balancing a ball on the tip of his nose in some circus or on a vaudeville stage. This fellow can live quite easily in fresh water.

The California sea lion inhabits almost the entire coast of California. At Point Lobos it is almost always seen in association with the more numerous Steller sea lion. The dark coloration, the "hump" on the forehead, and the bark which resembles that of a hound, are the characteristics that serve to distinguish this species. Apparently the two species are friendly, at least when on these rocky resting-places. Most of the time both Steller and California sea lions crowd together in "bunches," though the California species manages to stay fairly close together within the overall group. Two individuals of the same species sometimes snap at each other; not so frequently two of different species engage in a skirmish. Even the old males, who do most of the fighting, are timid if approached by a man.

Sea lions are usually seen hauled out on the rock surfaces above reach of the surf, lolling about, sprawled out, prone, with only rarely even a head raised. The animals seem to be sunning themselves, with no concern for any kind of outside disturbance. Counting them from the shore is almost impossible because the animals keep so close together, often appearing even to be across one another.

On the lower ledges, evidently just out of the water and still wet, they nearly always look shiny and dark-colored. The ones high on the rocks, apparently dry, are dull and golden brown in color. Seen swimming beneath the water they may appear distinctly green.

Steller sea lions are the largest of all sea lions—the average estimated weight of an adult male is about 1,400 pounds, and they measure from ten to eleven feet in length.

The sounds made by the Steller species when on the rocks are much like those made by a herd of cattle—possibly with a slightly lower tone. Sometimes they are deep-toned snoring sounds, as if the animals are growling in unison. On still nights these sounds can be heard easily at the entrance station at the inland edge of the Reserve.

California sea lions can usually be seen on Sea Lion Rocks offshore from Point Lobos. Their characteristic barking sound carries inland and can be heard throughout much of the Reserve.

When disturbed, the herd will generally rush off into the water in confusion, causing great commotion. After swimming about for awhile with raised heads the sea lions return to the rocks, which they climb easily.

Small groups of sea lions are often observed in Headland Cove in the surf, tumbling over one another, diving and coming up with their heads together. Apparently these maneuvers are in the nature of play.

Compact groups of sea lions are sometimes seen swimming at the surface of the water. They swim with an undulating motion (up and down), coming partly out of the water on each upward curve. Sometimes an animal comes up with such momentum that it emerges completely out of the water. Occasionally the head of one will be projected above the water and at times a front flipper will be extended upward into the air. Such compact groups of sea lions are followed by many birds, mostly Heermann and Western gulls.

Sea lions will also hunt in packs like wolves. Both of these species live on fish, squids, crabs, shellfish and devilfish or octopus; but the California sea lion eats comparatively few fish, while a sea lion of the Steller species makes fish the staple of its diet.

Harbor Seal[2]

In contrast to the large and noisy sea lions the less agile Harbor Seal is often missed by Reserve visitors, but is in fact resident there the year round in small numbers. Individuals range from four to six feet in length, depending on age and sex, and display great color variation, from blackish or dark brown through varying degrees of gray to some almost white animals. Most are mottled and are sometimes misnamed ''Leopard'' or ''Spotted'' seals.

They frequent bays and coves and can usually be observed at low tide hauled out on some favorite small rock or ledge, very close to the water. The best places to see them are the north shore of Headland Cove, the rocks bordering the channel between Bird Island and Pelican Point and rocks near the tip of Coal Chute Point. They are usually found in groups of half a dozen or less, and in the Reserve they do not consort with the sea lions. Pups may be seen from April to June. These seals rarely venture beyond the kelp beds and are known to eat fish, squid, octopus and some shellfish.

The California Gray Whale

At thirty-five to forty-five feet in length this is by far the largest animal to be seen in the Reserve. South Point is a good place from which to observe them as they pass beyond Seal Rocks along their annual migration route from summer feeding grounds in the Bering Sea to winter calving and breeding lagoons on the coast of Baja California. The southward movement takes place from mid-December to late February and the return, northward migration passes the Reserve during March and April, occasionally later. The best time to observe them is from Christmas to mid-January, and lighting conditions are normally most favorable in the morning and late afternoon. At these times the puffy ''blow'' or ''spout'' may be observed, followed by tail flukes as the animals sound. Occasionally an individual may breach, thrusting two-thirds of its body clear of the water, before falling back and creating a mighty splash. The whales travel in ''pods'' of one to five, occasionally more, at an average speed of some four knots. The navigational methods employed are not clearly understood.

This species was at one time heavily exploited. The whaling station, established in Whalers Cove in the 1860s, was based primarily on this species. The combination of inshore migration and slow speed made it possible for this species to be secured by small boats. It is now fully protected and increasing in numbers.

Somewhat timid and less active than sea lions, harbor seals frequently display their curiosity about people and seem to enjoy resting on small shoreline rocks such as this one in Sand Hill Cove.

Sea otter using its hand-like forepaws to grasp a sea urchin—one of its favorite food items.

The Killer Whale

This powerful animal, with its conspicuous dorsal fin, is a spectacular although irregular visitor to the Reserve. It is most often observed in the vicinity of Seal Rocks and the South Shore. Summer visits are more frequent, although they have occurred in every month. The size of the "pod" may vary from one to ten animals. Food is known to consist of fish, squid and seals. Even California gray whales may be killed on occasion.

The Elephant Seal

Increasing rapidly in California, this animal is an occasional visitor to the Reserve's beaches. Immature animals are more frequently seen than the more easily identified adult males.

Sea Otter[3]

The evolutionary achievement which enabled sea otters to survive in bitterly cold waters, ironically, also caused their near extinction by man; for these intelligent, industrious and often playful mammals had evolved the world's most valuable fur. The value and stylishness of this fur among Asians and Europeans was a major incentive for exploration and early settlement of the west coast of North America. Sea otter and fur seal hunting reached a climax in the first years of the 19th century when uncounted thousands of these animals were killed. Hunting began to decline as early as 1820 due to the increasing scarcity of otter and by 1850 they were considered rare.

In the early years of the 20th century sea otter were considered to be inevitably headed for extinction or else already gone. Therefore, in 1938 great excitement attended the sighting of a considerable number of otter living unobtrusively along the coast about eleven miles south of Point Lobos. Belatedly protected by an international treaty in 1911 and by a subsequent state law, the California sea otter were slowly recovering in number, and beginning to reoccupy part of their former range. They were finally sighted within the Point Lobos State Reserve in 1954. During roughly this same period of time small pockets of additional survivors were restocking sections of the Kurile and Aleutian island chains. During the last few years the recovery of this northern population has led to the reestablishment of the sea otter fur market with the Alaskan government allowing the harvest of about 500 pelts annually.

The sea otter is a member of the musteline family which includes weasel, mink, marten and other fur-bearing animals and is thus more closely related to the river otter than to other marine mammals. Adult males are about 4-1/2 feet long (including a ten to twelve inch long tail) and may weigh as much as eighty pounds. Adult females are slightly shorter and weigh about 45 pounds. Population increase is very slow inasmuch as the female ordinarily produces one pup at a time and in some years does not bear at all. Gestation time is thought to be about eight to ten months. About four years are required for a pup to reach maturity.

Otters groom and sleep while floating upon their backs in giant kelp and can best be recognized by their relatively

The Beechey ground squirrel is probably the most sociable small animal in the Reserve.

short length, their dog-like paws and flattened, furry-webbed feet, and by their characteristic hunting and feeding practices. One of the few mammal species to employ tools, sea otters often use small flat rocks as anvils for cracking large mussels and turban snails. Divers have seen otters dislodging food underwater by using rocks as hammers. Along with mussels and snails, their diet is likely to include crabs, chitons, abalones, sea stars, and urchins.

At the urging of commercial fishermen the Department of Fish and Game has undertaken a program of transplanting sea otter away from the southern limit of their present range where it is claimed that they adversely affect the supply of crab and abalone. Meanwhile, research on the little known biology of the otter is being conducted by the Department of Fish and Game as well as by the University of California at Santa Cruz.

A citizens' organization, "Friends of the Sea Otter" has been formed to assist in the development of a sound program of conservation for this fascinating, rare and still very possibly endangered animal species.

Ground Squirrel

Ground squirrels were once extremely numerous in Point Lobos Reserve and are still one of the most noticeable mammals in the area. They choose ground that is clothed with low vegetation, or has scattered boulders and bushes that can be used as lookout posts. They tend to prefer a slight slope, especially toward the east, where the soil is well-drained and where they can bask in the sunshine.

Squirrels attract predators to the Reserve and take alarm easily. Disturbed by a person, a squirrel may hurry off a short distance to a place where it can turn, sit on its hind legs, and stare at the disturber. When really frightened they give a sharp bark of alarm—a short, staccato whistling sound—and very quickly dive into their burrows, or into some other unobtrusive nook or cranny. Sentinels are then likely to station themselves on nearby lookout posts and courageously continue the alarm signals as long as the danger persists.

The burrowing of these animals keeps the ground well turned and aired. Foliage and green herbaceous plants supply them with food. They can often be seen sunning themselves in open places, and frequently members of a pair will chase each other in play while chattering rapidly.

Gray Squirrel

The gray squirrel is one of the conspicuous mammals in the Reserve, partly because of its large size and fearless disposition, partly because it is active in the daytime throughout the whole year, and partly because of the everpresent signs of its home and feeding habits. Estimates of the total number of gray squirrels in this area vary upwards from one hundred, depending upon the time of year.

One word——pines——is enough to characterize the habitat of the gray squirrel at Point Lobos. They are found all through the pine woods and none of them is seen very far from a pine tree. In these trees all the essential needs of this animal are fulfilled. The branches provide safe refuge from ground-prowling predators; also in the tops of the trees there is support and material for nests.

These squirrels are closely dependent upon pine seeds for their food supply, though they are not restricted to this one source. They are often seen, both on the ground and in the trees, carrying fresh cones, which they almost invariably grasp firmly by the base with the small end pointed forward. In order to gain access to cones out on the end of limbs, it is often necessary for squirrels to cut off obstructing small branches and stems, which fall to the ground, making a conspicuous litter. The squirrels do not strip the bark, but make a clean cut. The greatest amount of this cutting seems to occur in mid-April. Another food source for gray squirrels in the Reserve is the acorn crop on the live oak trees. They crawl sometimes to the very tips of some of the outermost branches, and there they hang head downward, holding on only with their hind feet. Having cut an acorn off with its incisors, a squirrel will back up or turn around to reach a more secure position. The acorn is then transferred to its forefeet and the squirrel proceeds to hull and eat it. Gray squirrels also feed on the upper part of large toadstools which are abundant during the rainy season.

Gray squirrels can go all through the woods without coming to the ground, following along familiar overhead "paths" without hesitation, jumping across the interval between branches of adjacent treetops as much as fifty feet above the ground.

The response of gray squirrels to the near presence of humans varies widely. Usually they retreat to safety, but sometimes they protest loudly by barking and sometimes by rapping on the wood with their forefeet. One gray squirrel during the original Point Lobos study came directly to an observer who was sitting stock-still with his back against a pine trunk at the edge of Mound Meadow. The squirrel climbed onto his knee, looked him in the eye for about two seconds, then without any appearance of sudden alarm, took a course without haste back into the woods.

Pocket Gopher

On approximately one-third of the land[4] at Point Lobos pocket gophers play the predominant part in modifying the physical character of the upper soil as well as in affecting the plant life and, less directly, the animal life there. They avoid three general types of ground: (1) the forest where there are few small roots; (2) the wet, soggy ground, where they cannot keep dry; (3) the oldest, longest established grassland, where,

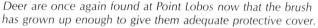

The white-footed mouse, Peromyscus maniculatus, a six to eight inch long native of North America, is nocturnal and therefore seldom seen. It eats seeds and insects, and inhabits wooded or brushy areas.

Deer are once again found at Point Lobos now that the brush has grown up enough to give them adequate protective cover.

Juvenile elephant seals are seen from time to time at Point Lobos. An adult breeding colony of these animals now exists on Año Nuevo Island to the north. Below, a harem of Steller sea lions, dominated by a fully mature bull left of center. A newly born pup can be seen in the lower right.

possibly, the sod is composed of roots too fibrous to be suitable as gopher food. The abundance of herbaceous plants with thick stems and roots provides ample food. Salt grass, occurring in patches in Mound Meadow, is the preferred provender of the pocket gopher.

An estimate of the average number of these animals within the Reserve during a year in which they were closely observed (1934-35) was about one thousand. A population-regulating factor of great significance in long-time processes is the presence of predators such as the barn owl.

The extent of the ground workings of a pocket gopher is shown by counts made on an area three paces long by 2-1/3 paces wide, where there were sixty-four eruptions—fresh ones since the last rain. These varied from mounds of normally large size down to holes plugged level with the surface, where stems of grass had been trimmed off above ground. This was evidently all the work of one gopher.

Harvest Mouse

The harvest mouse is one of the most numerous rodents in the Reserve. These mice are abundant in late summer and fall in all the types of grassland, even on the most recently grass-covered ground. In summer and fall they may be found in the pine woods, especially where the floor is covered with grass; and pine needles, sections of logs, and remains of stumps provide refuge places for them. The bush-covered slopes of Vierras Knoll are well populated with these mice.

Their nests are globular in form, the top well above the ground, but nearly always well-concealed from above with a loose thatching of grass or brush.

Meadow Mouse

In mats of dead grass and other plant material, meadow mice make a network of runways, which, during the year, extend to nearly every section of the Reserve. They are present in great numbers not only in the grassland, but throughout the brush-land habitat. They are also quite numerous on the floor of the pine woods.

Several kinds of hawks fly back and forth across the meadow mouse colonies, obviously watching for opportunities to make a kill. These mice can be caught at almost any time because they work both during daylight hours and at night. In fact, the marked increase in numbers of hawks on the area through the summer can be attributed largely to increased numbers of mice.

Amphibians and Reptiles

Slender salamanders occur in small numbers throughout the pine woods .and on certain portions of the grassland.

The Pacific tree toad is apparently the most numerous species of amphibian at Point Lobos though the absence of permanent freshwater ponds has limited their development. Tadpoles have been found in many temporary ponds, but as these dry up rather rapidly, the tadpoles do not often have time to transform into frogs before the water is gone.

Fence lizards are the commonest species of reptile in the Reserve. They live in a variety of situations from near the edge of the water on the beach back through the pine timber. They sun themselves on the sandstone cliffs and granite boulders as well as on cypress and pine logs.

Snakes are relatively rare. So far as is known, no venomous snakes have been seen here.

Other Noteworthy Mammals

Numerous raccoon tracks have been found on the sand at Gibson Beach, indicating that they have gone all over the beach and especially to the drift masses of kelp and edges of rocks along the tide line.

Striped skunks live in the Reserve in some numbers along with jack rabbits.[5] The presence of wood rats in the Reserve is chiefly revealed by their nests, found in the pine woods, mostly among the live oaks there, but also in thickets of Ceanothus and poison oak, and among the cypresses. These nests are built of soft materials such as leaves and grass, but they are piled over with coarse sticks, twigs and leaves, sometimes to a height of several feet. The nests then resemble a dead bush under growing bushes.

Deer are a prominent feature at Point Lobos too, now. And in those years when they are most abundant bobcats are often seen.

Amphibians and Reptiles Found in Point Lobos Reserve

Slender Salamander — *Batrachoseps attenuatus*
Oregon Salamander — *Ensatina eschscholtzii*
Arboreal Salamander — *Aneides lugubris*
California Toad — *Bufo boreas*
Pacific Tree Toad — *Hyla regilla*
Fence Lizard — *Sceloporus occidentalis*
Alligator Lizard — *Gerrhonotus multicarinatus*
Gopher Snake — *Pituophis catenifer*
Garter Snake — *Thamnophis ordinoides*
Yellow-bellied Racer — *Coluber constrictor*

---

1 — When the Reserve was first established in 1933 it included just 354 acres. In 1960 seven hundred seventy-five underwater acres adjacent to the Reserve were designated as the nation's first "underwater reserve." In 1962 one hundred twenty-four upland acres were added to the Reserve in order to protect a "pygmy forest" made up of dwarfed Gowen cypress. As a result of these and several smaller acquisitions the current total acreage of the Reserve including land and water is now 1,255 acres.

2 — Information on the harbor seal, gray whale, killer whale and elephant seal was supplied for this revised edition of the Point Lobos Reserve book by Alan Baldridge of the Hopkins Marine Station.

3 — Information on sea otter was supplied by J. E. Vandevere, of the University of California at Santa Cruz, especially for inclusion in the revised edition of this book.

4 — This statement was made in 1935 when more of the Reserve was still grassland.

5 — As of 1970 jack rabbits have long since become quite rare and brush rabbits have become numerous. This change is due in large part to changes in vegetation within the Reserve.

Western gulls can be seen the year around at Point Lobos.

VIII

Birds of Shore & Sea

Joseph Grinnell / Jean M. Linsdale

POINT LOBOS RESERVE is a veritable haven of refuge and an expansive banquet table for the birds. At all times, they gather there in great numbers. Some are year-round inhabitants, some are seasonal, and some are merely wayfarers bound for more distant fields. The "through" migration of land birds, however, is surprisingly weak. In the main, arrivals and departures become evident only in spring and fall, and these movements take place gradually over a period of many weeks. There is no migratory "rush" at all. The winter and spring population is heavier than the summer population; furthermore the birds seem to leave the Reserve after the nesting season, before the food supply has been noticeably reduced.

Birds occupy all the habitats of the Reserve. Of the 147 kinds of birds noted by Grinnell and Linsdale, twenty-eight percent of the species listed owe their presence directly to the influence of the ocean.

On the shore, turnstones, oystercatchers, and other shorebirds, as well as such land birds as Audubon warbler and black phoebe, forage regularly. Some pelagic cormorants roost and nest on certain nearly vertical, conglomerate cliffs, as also do a few cliff swallows, and occasionally black phoebes and duck hawks. This use is evidently because of freedom of the sites from disturbance, and the suitability of the niches and shelves for nests. Several islands support nesting colonies of Brandt and pelagic cormorants, and pigeon guillemots. The largest, Bird Island, near the southern boundary of the Reserve, is used as a kind of headquarters by a colony of brown pelicans. Several pairs of black oystercatchers and many Western gulls also generally nest on the islands.

Ocean Birds

Brown Pelican

Conspicuous among all the birds in the Reserve, the brown pelicans make their home on Bird Island. Only known breeding colony of these birds north of the Channel Islands, it is likely to remain the home site of large numbers of them if left undisturbed by man.[1]

These large, peculiarly constructed birds are here the year around, although during late winter and early spring there may be days when no pelican is in sight. Probably 200 or more are more or less permanent residents, but in many years during the early autumn, a kind of travel season begins with a great influx of pelicans from colonies on islands of Lower California and the mainland of Mexico. As many as 3,000 pelicans have been known to gather on these rocks by the late fall, probably attracted by the resident birds, and the favorable roosting site.

They are quite easily seen from shore as they tend to gather on the leeward side of the rocks, where they are somewhat protected from the wind. This is particularly true in winter.

The breeding cycle of the pelicans has not been definitely determined, because no one goes out to the rocks any more for fear of disturbing the birds; but from mainland observation it seems that they begin to pair off as early as February. By April some of the nests are built, and by May there are two or three eggs (sometimes, though, only one) in each nest.

The nest building procedure is for one bird to stay on the spot while the other goes for material, collecting sticks and weed stems. Then, standing beside the nest spot, it opens its bill and shakes out the sticks and stems, which are taken and arranged by the sitting mate. The highest sites seem to be most desired, for the birds crowd there and are most active in driving away intruders.

Nests on Bird Island are situated mostly in compact groups on the north end, the middle hump, and the foot of the south hump. The birds relieve the monotony of incubation by frequently stretching and preening. Sometimes they flap their wings hard enough to blow the feathers of a neighbor.

The number of young hatched on Bird Island varies greatly from year to year. Since 1927 the number has ranged from none to seventy-eight.

The naked young are kept covered by the brooding parent and are not often seen, though young pelicans have been observed feeding from the open bill and pouch of their parents. The young are fed in this way until they are able to fish for themselves—even as late as August and September of the year.

Pelicans occasionally can be seen fishing in the narrow channel between Seal Rocks and the mainland and in the general vicinity of the tip of Cypress Point. However, the greatest number appear to fly off to some more distant place to the northward. The birds both leaving and returning usually fly close to the water, at times seeming almost to touch the waves.

When food is sighted, the procedure noted most often is for the bird to turn back and drop to the surface of the water, then to make quick jabs with its opened bill—sometimes only a few and at other times many. Only on rare occasions have

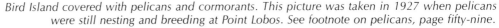

Bird Island covered with pelicans and cormorants. This picture was taken in 1927 when pelicans were still nesting and breeding at Point Lobos. See footnote on pelicans, page fifty-nine.

the pelicans been seen to go partially or completely below the water.

A striking feature of the behavior of the brown pelican is its marked trait of flying over the ocean and avoiding the mainland during the early part of the year. Grinnell and Linsdale guessed that this was either because of the economy of flying over prospective fishing areas or because they felt a greater degree of safety when over the water.[2]

Brandt Cormorant and Pelagic Cormorant

These two species, not easily distinguished from each other by many visitors, offer continuous demonstration of two diverse ways of coping with one environment by separate, closely related species, both of which are present here in abundance, though they are not readily observable at many other places along the Pacific Coast.

Greater numbers of Brandt cormorants nest at Point Lobos than of any other ocean bird. Because these birds like to perch and nest on the outer seaward sides of rocks and islands, it is practically impossible to count the numbers present; but it has been estimated that between 300 and 500 individuals live within the limits of the Reserve—that is, during the nesting season, when the greatest numbers are present.

They can be seen on the tops of all "humps" of islands, and quite often they form a fringe of thick black dots along the skyline of almost the whole of Bird Island, which is by no means the exclusive property of the brown pelicans.

A marked change in the behavior of the adults in the colonies is noted as the season progresses. At an early date, before the "nest-situations" are well defined, the birds are unstable and easily frightened from the rock. Later they become fixed in their positions and are not readily disturbed from them.

By March the birds begin to gather green land plants and sea plants for their nests. The sea plants are secured generally from the coves, where they dive to the bottom for about thirty-five seconds or so, and come up with the nesting material in their bills. They also get nest material by thieving from each other.

By late May the birds can be seen on their nests, and by the end of June the young are hatched and only a few broken nests remain. In July great flocks of Brandt cormorants have been seen flying northward, past Point Lobos and over Carmel Bay.

Brandt cormorants can be seen at nearly all times at the Reserve, either on the islands, in flight close above the water, or diving for food.

Pelagic cormorants are much less numerous than the Brandt variety. They are also smaller, more slender, with thinner necks and heads, and their wing-beats in flight are more rapid than the Brandt cormorants. Roosting and nesting places are in the sides of cliffs along the shore of the Point. Groups do not generally reach more than 100 individuals. When the nesting season arrives, pelagic cormorants evidently break up into smaller groups than when roosting.

One or more pelagic cormorants feeding or in flight usually can be seen by watching for a few minutes at almost

Brown pelican in flight.

Pigeon Guillemots.

Cormorants:
Pelagic cormorant
on the left,
Brandt's cormorants
on the right.

Sanderlings.

any place along the shore. A favorite feeding spot for certain individuals is Whalers Cove, where they catch fish and occasionally bring up a crab from the depths.

Western Gull

Among the several kinds of gulls, only this one is a permanent resident at Point Lobos. Its large numbers and aggressive nature make it important here in the animal community along the shore. It is seen in all parts of the area—in the water and on the islands and rocks close to shore, on the ground close to shore, or in flight anywhere, very often over the woods.

The Western gull searches over a wide variety of forage ground. One favorite source of food is the refuse left at tables by picnickers and along the shore by fishermen. Another type of forage niche of a more nearly natural sort, and rather peculiar to gulls, may be noticed often during low tide. Along the sea cliffs where the rock surfaces rise vertically out of deep water, single, scattered Western gulls commonly feed over the rocks uncovered at low tide, as well as at certain favorable spots on the ocean away from the shore.

The breeding season is a long one. By August most of the young gulls are in dark plumage and able to fly, although they still beg for food from the adults. As late as December young gulls have alighted beside adult birds, have opened their bills near the heads of the older gulls and have uttered high pleading notes, though the older birds generally ignore them by this time. The adults occasionally remain stationed at nesting sites until fall, even after the young have gone.

Land Birds

POINT LOBOS RESERVE lies in what may be termed a *Transition Life Zone.* To the north is the Boreal and to the south is the Austral Zone. Vertebrates typical of both zones are found at Point Lobos, though sixty percent of them belong to Austral species, and only twenty-six percent to the Boreal. In addition there are some species present—like the Allen hummingbird, Western flycatcher, violet-green swallow, pigmy nuthatch, and purple finch—about fourteen percent, which belong specifically to the Transition Zone itself. The last percentage is fairly normal for Transition anywhere; for this zone is essentially merely one of overlap between Austral (or Sonora) and Boreal (in its Canadian division).

Allen Hummingbird

The busy Allen hummingbird, flitting rapidly from flower to flower, hovering over a blossom to take the nectar, always attracts attention. Of Austral Zone origin, the bird is of peculiar interest because, in spite of its great powers of flight individually and its seasonal migrations, it is restricted in its breeding to an astonishingly narrow range—to the "fog-belt" of California, from the Oregon line to San Luis Obispo County. Nests

have been found beyond these limits but rarely. These hummingbirds are not known to nest farther than twenty miles from the sea.

The species has no counterpart in the Sierra Nevada; though it does have in the coast belt north of California. The life zone is thus chiefly Transition.

Males and females of this species occupy separate types of environment nearly all the time. Grinnell and Linsdale, at the time of their study of Point Lobos, thought some fifteen females lived in the area then, but not more than one-third this number of males.

Chestnut-backed Chickadee

The chestnut-backed chickadee, characterized by rusty or chestnut-colored sides, is found in pine forests all along the Pacific Coast lowlands from Alaska to Southern California. When a survey was made in 1935, there were about fifty chestnut-backed chickadees resident within the Reserve. Foraging places for these birds include all of the kinds of trees found here. Nesting begins in March and the bob-tailed young ones can usually be seen in May. A characteristic of their nesting sites, which are from four to ten feet from the ground in cavities in stumps of rotted pines, is that practically all of them are closely surrounded by thickets of young pines or are screened by low boughs of taller trees. As a result, the nest entrance, while close to the ground, is hidden from view. The birds contribute to the concealment by making quick silent flights to the nests without any pause at the entrance. By nesting at this low level the chickadees avoid the slightly higher level or zone normally inhabited by the very aggressive, fiercely competitive pigmy nuthatches.

Pigmy Nuthatch

Visitors are attracted to birds of this species because of their almost continuous notes, and also because of their large numbers and gregarious habits. As many as a hundred of these small birds will be here in nesting season, though they are present in some numbers throughout the year. The nesting period is a long one, preparation of nests sometimes beginning in February. Nuthatches dig their nesting cavities in pines or the dead remains of pines. The sites selected are high ones, averaging thirty feet above the ground and running as high as sixty feet. While the nuthatch and the chickadee have about the same forage beat and cruising radius, often indeed seem closely associated, the nuthatch seeks (at least in the season of greatest food scarcity) static insect food in crevices of dry cones, twigs, and smaller branches, and it uses its specialized digging tool, the bill, to dislodge or uncover these insects. In other words, the nuthatch has a food source beyond the usual reach of the chickadee. And then, too, with suitably rotted boles of trees available, it digs its own nesting cavity.

Pigmy nuthatches appear always to dig hurriedly and persistently. Bluebirds are the most formidable competitors of this species for nest sites, and in several instances, in which the entrances were of sufficient size, they have temporarily or even permanently ousted the smaller birds from the cavity.

Mature screech owl.

Hummingbird
feeding
its young.

Wren-tit.

Bush-tit

The flock behavior and peculiar nesting traits of this Western bird make it one of the permanent attractions, especially to visitors acquainted with birds in other regions.

Bush-tits are present continuously throughout the year at Point Lobos. About 100 are around at the beginning of the nesting season. All through the winter, bush-tits are seen in flocks averaging about fifteen birds each.

Their nest-building season starts late in February and most of the nests contain young as late as the latter part of April. Bush-tits build nests in a wide variety of plants, nearly every kind of tree and bush in the area being used, which is a peculiar characteristic in any bird.

House Finch

The fact that the linnet, or house finch, is so widely abundant through the farmed portions of California makes more significant the added fact that it is also a prominent feature of the landscape at Point Lobos. At this locality we may expect to learn the true nature of the adaptation of the bird to its normal surroundings. It is one of the few kinds of animals to make important use of the cypresses.

The house finch is one of the most conspicuous singing birds, and is just about the last species of bird to be quieted by a cold and overcast sky. In the building of nests, the usual procedure seems to be for the female to gather and carry to the nest most of the materials, and for the male to accompany her and sing. The house finch uses lichen for the main construc-

tion of the nest, generally building on the limbs of trees, although sometimes cavities and crannies in stumps are used instead. Both pines and cypresses are occupied by their nests, which are usually well concealed among lichens or masses of trash on tops of flat limbs or boughs. Approximately five weeks, starting generally in April, are required for nesting, from the beginning of building until the nest is left.

Ordinarily finches exhibit a marked preference for open places, exposed to the sunshine. They frequently feed in compact flocks of fifty or more. Their fare is ripening seeds and other parts of the plants, particularly of the mustard and radish. Often they hull and discard outer coverings of the seeds.

House finches are present at Point Lobos throughout the year, but in varying numbers. They are most numerous during the early part of the nesting season, when they are the most numerous species, with the possible exception of the colonial cliff swallow. It is estimated that around the middle of May at least 800 individual finches live in the Reserve.

White-crowned Sparrow

This bird is a conspicuous feature of that narrow coastal portion of California typified by Point Lobos. It is predominant in the brushland, and its welfare here requires freedom from disturbance by unnatural changes in this type of habitat.

Approximately 150 pairs are found in the Reserve at the beginning of the nesting season.

All through the year this bird stays in the same general type of habitat—the bush-covered portions of the Reserve. All kinds of bushes are occupied to some extent, but lupines appear to be more suitable than any other. This bird forages a great deal on the ground between, and a short distance out from, the bushes, as well as within their foliage. It returns to the bushes for cover and for lookouts from which it can see approaching dangers. General types of food obtained in these situations vary widely, including as they do the ripened seeds of the plants, the green leaves of plants, and insects. It is especially interesting to watch the scattered flocks forage out over the open ground, yet keeping close to the bushes.

These sparrows sing much during the spring, with a clear, full song, and occasionally they are heard at night, and during the summer.

Raptorial Birds — Hawks, Eagles, Owls

Thirteen species of hawks, eagles, and owls have been observed at Point Lobos. These birds exert steady pressure on the populations of smaller animals and thus they provide the necessary curb to over-population by such creatures. The surest means for keeping the raptors is to maintain, uninvaded by trails, roads, and other human works, certain habitat "reservoirs." Suitable ones occur only in the main area of pine woods and in the vicinity of Whalers Knoll. It seems certain that the visits of golden eagles are due to the presence of these "reservoirs," and to ground squirrels as a food source appropriate to this large bird of prey.

Red-tailed hawks are seen occasionally as are sparrow hawks, a species of hawk that is known to nest and to maintain very nearly continuous residence within the Reserve.

Though the sharp-shinned hawk is not such a frequent visitor to the Reserve, encounters with one by even the casual observer are likely to be remembered. When the hawk makes a dash there is a frantic exodus of small birds from the vicinity, and they are loath to leave cover for some time after a sharp-shinned hawk has been sighted.

Grinnell and Linsdale reported that during their study of the area, one or two or three golden eagles occasionally visited Point Lobos from somewhere off to the east. An encounter between an eagle and two duck hawks was watched in the early afternoon of March 30, 1935. The eagle appeared to be looking for ground squirrels near the parking place by the base of Cypress Point. It flew westward, sailing with the wind until it came nearly to a cliff where there were two pere-

grine falcons — or duck hawks. When these birds came out the eagle promptly turned back landward, the falcons diving at it alternately, one or the other screaming constantly. At least three times, as a falcon dashed down at the eagle, the eagle rolled over so as to meet the assault from above, with talons extended upward toward the attacker. It could not be seen that there was actual contact at any moment, but the eagle was obviously on the defensive and made for the woods with heavily beating wings, soon disappearing into the woods toward Rat Hill. Only then did the falcons give up the pursuit and fly back to the cliff.

These observers also reported that in the fall for a month beginning on September 21st, from one to three golden eagles were present regularly in the Reserve. They were seen mostly in the vicinity of Whalers Knoll, along the western margin of the pines, and over the open ground west of there. They seemed to be occupied mainly with hunting for ground squirrels. One was seen once on the ground among bushes. Some days these birds were heard calling almost continuously. Apparently when the numbers of ground squirrels above ground were reduced at the beginning of the season of hibernation, the eagles moved off the area, at least for most of their activities.

Duck hawks keep to the seaward sides of Point Lobos and particularly Little Dome and Big Dome. On every occasion that a duck hawk appears over land there is much confusion among the small birds, followed by several minutes of complete silence.[3]

Owls are also steady predators in this Reserve.

The birds here discussed are perhaps the most important to Point Lobos Reserve because of their great numbers, their effects upon the flora and fauna of the area, or their high degree of adaptation to the environmental conditions within the Reserve. However, many others attract the eye or the ear of visitors with their unusual characteristics or delightful songs.

Oregon juncos with their black heads and rust-colored backs, Steller's jays with handsome crests and deep-blue plumage, thrashers, killdeer, meadowlarks, finches, thrushes, plump quails calling "Who are you? Who are you?," sanderlings and turnstones running in and out with the waves — these are but a few of the more obvious birds to be seen and enjoyed by those who visit Point Lobos State Reserve.

1 — Pelicans no longer nest on Bird Island, but this description by Grinnell and Linsdale has now taken on special historical significance.

2 — As of this printing (1970) pelicans are still frequently seen at Point Lobos though it is estimated that they are only about half as numerous as they once were. It is significant that there have been no pelican eggs hatched on Bird Island since 1959, and no pelican nests there since 1966. Some observers have felt that this was due to the harassment of these birds by thoughtless, rock-throwing Reserve visitors, along with the repeated disruptions caused by low-flying aircraft. At the same time, however, an increasing wealth of evidence points to the role of DDT and other related chlorinated hydrocarbon pesticides as the primary cause of pelican population decline.

It is known that DDT and other persistant pesticides have been dispersed to every part of the earth's surface, and that these pesticides are collected and concentrated by the plants and animals that make up the food chains leading to the higher animals. Because of their diet, and certain other ecological factors, pelicans are especially vulnerable to DDT and other persistant pesticides. Though there are still a large number of pelicans along the coast it is now thought that present levels of pesticide contamination may inevitably and irreversibly lead to the total extinction of these wild birds. Recent evidence indicates that

this could occur without the death of significant numbers of adult birds because DDT and other related, persistant pesticides apparently have a damaging effect upon estrogen secretion — a lesson that has ominous, long-range implications for human beings as well as wild birds. In pelicans this estrogenic disruption has a direct effect upon calcium production leading to the formation of eggs with shells so thin they cannot be successfully incubated.

3 — This account by Grinnell and Linsdale is of considerable and perhaps even increasing historical interest inasmuch as peregrine falcons have not nested in the Reserve since the early 1950's and are now very rarely seen there. In fact, though wild peregrines were once one of the most widely distributed animals in the world they are now very rapidly disappearing not only from California but from all their natural habitats around the world.

A favorite with "noble-men" hunters throughout the middle ages, the royal bird of ancient Egypt, and still popular with falconers, the peregrine is now apparently headed for extinction — at least in the wild state. Experts cite various contributing causes, but as with pelicans there is increasing evidence that DDT and the other persistent, chlorinated hydrocarbon pesticides are the primary problem.

IX

Life Between the Tides

Walter K. Fisher / James L. Leitch

Walter K. Fisher was on the faculty of Stanford University and Director of the Hopkins Marine Station in Pacific Grove for thirty-three years. An active conservationist, he was a member of the original Point Lobos Advisory Committee and the author of numerous articles about invertebrates of the Pacific Ocean. He is perhaps best known for his definitive, three-volume work on North Pacific starfishes.

James L. Leitch, a research associate in zoology, served as an assistant to Walter K. Fisher at the time of the original Point Lobos Advisory Committee study. His extensive field observations at Point Lobos supplied much of the information on which this chapter is based.

*T*HE INTERTIDAL ANIMALS of Point Lobos are a fair sample of those which inhabit exposed rocky shores from Central California to Southern Alaska. Ledges of hard rock thrust fan-wise into cold turbulent water. Waves rush into narrow coves, dash high, and fall back in numberless cascades. Except on the southern shore, where irregularities of the eroded conglomerate provide shelter from the heaviest surges, there is little chance for the formation of sizable tide pools and, hence, for tide-pool associations at their best. The sides of the granite points are steep and offer maximum resistance to the buffeting and scouring action of great seas, which in winter assail the coast with spectacular force until the ocean is churned to whiteness.

Under such conditions the only life which can survive is that adapted by toughness to withstand shock, and by structure to adhere either temporarily or permanently. Of course, many creatures are sheltered within rock crevices, between closely crowded mussels, or in masses of kelp such as *Laminaria.*

Along the lower, southern shore of the Point the conglomerate rock is much broken, affording a great variety of exposures, and often complete shelter. At one place there is a small rocky beach uncovered at low tide. Here and on Punta de los Lobos Marinos will be found a considerable number of small tide pools, the population of which varies with exposure to surf and position above the lowest tide level. In general, pools nearest low water and least exposed to wave action contain the greatest variety of forms.

It need hardly be stressed that the time to observe shore animals is during low water and when the Pacific is living up to its name. High tide or high seas are avoided by the old hand. At such times it is dangerous, especially where the footing is difficult, to approach too near the water, owing to the occurrence of sporadic giant waves which greatly overreach the average and constitute a serious peril to inexperienced persons.

Animal life between tides is dominated by the invertebrates—creatures lacking a backbone—such as the sponges, anemones, worms, mollusks, barnacles, crabs, sea stars, sea urchins, sea squirts, and numerous other less conspicuous types.

On wave-swept, exposed rock such as the granite pyramid known as The Pinnacle, three rather conspicuous intertidal zones are readily observable. There is a broad, somewhat bare, splash zone mostly above mean high tide; a broad dark zone of mussels and kelp; and below this a coralline zone exposed only at lowest tide and colored pinkish or reddish. On *protected* shores this lowest zone is very populous.

The middle zone owes much of its characteristic dark color to beds of California mussels, which also cover the tops of some of the rocks off the north shore, submerged at high tide.

The lower part of the mussel zone is covered by a dense growth of the tough brown kelp, *Laminaria*.

The hardy goose barnacle (*Policipes*) grows in clusters among the mussels. Its peduncle or stem is really its head by which it is cemented to rocks. Its gregarious habit affords mutual protection against the pounding or shearing action of waves. Feeding on both of these animals, unbothered by the heavy seas, the common sea star finds the roughest coast a congenial habitat. It clings to the rock by means of its hundreds of sucker feet. It is purple, brown, or yellow in color.

The closely crowded mussels are attached to the rocks by tough, horny threads which are spun by the long, protrusible, finger-like foot. The broadened end of the mussel is turned outward and receives the impact of waves, but between the inner tapered ends of the mussels (next to the surface of the rocks), there are little galleries filled with relatively quiet water; a situation rather like that when a strong wind passes over a thick forest but does not greatly disturb the quietness near the ground. In these irregular arcade-like spaces live a multitude of worms: Various unsegmented flatworms; nemerteans, soft and rubbery; segmented green nereids, armed with jaws and remotely resembling centipedes;

Halosydna with two rows of scales along the back; sipunculids, sometimes called "peanut worms." A great variety of small crustaceans, isopods, amphipods, small crabs and shrimps are also regular denizens of the mussel beds, as are certain small mollusks.

Chitons (*Nattalina* and *Katharina*) are found in and around the mussel zone along with limpets, reddish volcano barnacles, rock barnacles; and in any little chance rock pool, greenish sea anemones, hermit crabs, and sometimes small purple sea urchins. In more sheltered nooks or on quiet days the two sorts of shore crabs venture alertly from hiding. They are unbelievably nimble, and merit the name "Sally Lightfoot" aptly bestowed by West Indians on a near relative of identical habits.

In the uppermost zone, wet only by spray, are dingy little littorine snails crowded in crevices for mutual protection and moisture, small limpets, and (once upon a time) the large owl limpet, too, beloved of shell collectors and certain gourmets.

In this wave-swept area, below the mussel zone, the rocks are often covered with a reddish incrustation, the alga *Lithophyton*. In *protected crevices* there are red, yellow, and blue

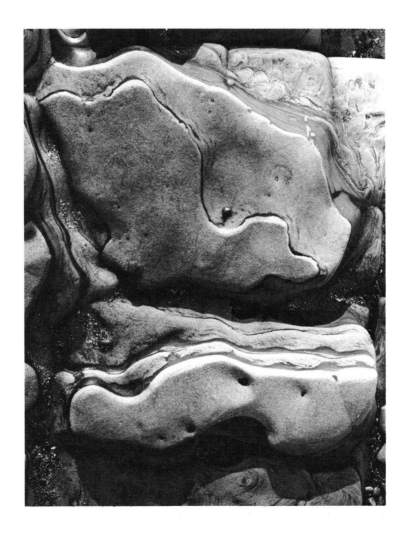

encrusting sponges; delicate feathery growths—the hydroids and bryozoans; soft brown colonial sea squirts; small sea cucumbers, and naked mollusks of high color. Also found here are quite a range of mollusks including the black abalone, key-hole limpets, leafy horn-mouth snail, top shells, and others. Where the rock is not too vertical, purple urchins occur, often in individual "forms" hollowed from the rock. These little basins are excavated by the urchins, which cling tightly with sucker feet and braced spines.

A characteristic feature of the most wave-swept offshore rocks are the miniature groves of sea palms, *Postelsia*, graceful kelps of unbelievable toughness which bend in unison when a surge breaks over them, and then spring upright as the water cascades from among the closely crowded stems. They favor flat-topped rocks and benches at about mid-tide and are annuals—destroyed by winter storms and renewed in the spring.

On *protected rocky shores* many animals of the exposed coast are present, along with a multitude of others that are unable to survive the rigors of heavy wave action. Provided there is an ample supply of well-aerated water at or near sea temperature—the more varied the configuration of the shore the greater will be the variety of life. In the most favorable situations on Point Lobos a fair representation of the intertidal invertebrates of Northern California can be seen.

A sheltered, fairly deep, tide pool with its surrounding rocks and cobbles can house a rather formidable list of animals. One of the first to strike the eye is the giant green sea anemone, very flower-like with its several circles of tentacles, which normally are extended to trap unwary crabs or sculpins. Green anemones six to ten inches in diameter are very old—fifty to 100 years—and should be treated with respect. These sea anemones are not fastidious; any small animal will do—provided it is not strong enough to escape the adhesive tentacles that fold slowly inward.

There is a smaller, related, dull pink species of anemone, as well as a rare, deep-carmine one with large tentacles, sometimes called sea dahlia. A fourth species, the most common anemone, is quite small, greenish, and grows, in mats. It covers itself with bits of shell and squirts water from a multitude of pores when it contracts. It is usually found somewhat higher in relation to the tide than is the green variety—which, by the way, is also an animated watering pot.

Belonging in the same group as the anemones are the exquisite hydroids, delicate miniature trees and bushes flowering in medusa heads. They are white, yellow, orange; others are brownish, as the ostrich feather, *Aglaophenia*.

Often living alongside the green anemone are purple urchins. The larger, maroon, giant urchins, with longer spines, are inhabitants of the deepest pools and are most common offshore. Young purple urchins are green and usually hide under stones or in crevices. Both feed on kelp. In shallow pools the purple ones cover themselves with bits of shell and kelp which they hold in place with their sucker feet.

The common sea star found in mussel beds is equally at home in quiet tide pools. Its name, *Pisaster ochraceus*, is rather misleading, as it is more often brown or dull purple than yellow. It is a voracious predator, but is too sluggish to capture anything unattached—hence its predilection for mussels, barnacles, and limpets. The multi-rayed star (*Pycnopodia helianthodies*) can move rapidly and execute countermovements actively when excited by food. When under "full sail" with its thousands of tube feet lashing back and forth it is an impressive animal. Its numerous cushions, made up of millions of microscopic pincers, along with its wide, flexible body make it a formidable predator. By preference it devours both species of sea urchins, swallowing them whole, spines and all. After twenty-four to thirty-six hours, the cleaned test and spines are ejected through the mouth. A large specimen, two feet in diameter with twenty to twenty-three rays, has about 15,000 tube feet, all perfectly coordinated so that the star can crawl with any ray foremost. It has a wide range of color: purplish gray, dull furry gray, orange, reddish.

Two kinds of six-rayed starlets, upward of 2-1/2 inches in diameter, are found under rocks and are notable for brooding their developing eggs and tiny young. A temporary brood-chamber is formed around the mouth by arching the disk and approximating the bases of the rays. An arctic relative swallows its eggs and the young develop in the stomach. The small blood star, *Henricia*, is also found under stones. It has five rays and incubates its young.

In the short-rayed bat star (*Patiria*) the body is sometimes rather thick and inflated, sometimes depressed, without sharp distinction between disk and rays, which may also number 4, 6, or 7 instead of the prevalent five. The color is yellow below; bright red, dark red, purple, straw-color, blue gray, greenish gray above, or sometimes a mosaic of all of them.

Among the crabs and crab-like animals of tide pools and the intertidal zone are two shore crabs, the green-lined Pachygrapsus and the purple Hemigrapsus, with squarish shells. They are agile scavengers, often hiding by day under stones or in crevices. The first usually has a dark green shell, the second a purplish one, the claws spotted with purple. Under stones will be found the flattened, brown, active, porcelain crab (*Petrolisthes*) with long antennae; and in deeper parts of a pool any of several very sluggish spider crabs, often overgrown with sponges and hydroids. Of the "edible crabs," *Cancer productus* is most likely to be found. It is striped in youth, but rusty red when adult.

Hermit crabs, inhabiting empty mollusk shells, are the clowns of any tide pool. They are active, pugnacious, inquisitive. The commonest has blue tips to the legs, and often lives in black turban shells. A large relative of the garden sow bug, the rock louse (*Ligiada occidentalis*) will be found well above water, foraging on rocks or in crevices, its gait unpleasantly reminiscent of the cockroach. On kelps, under stones, and in sand are numerous other isopods, some very small. Among the true shrimps the most amazing is the pistol shrimp which dwells among sponges, kelps, and surf grass, often in very definite tunnels. The thumb of the large mitten-like claw is adapted to snap against the palm. This is the source of those little snapping noises that can sometimes be heard at low tide.

The most conspicuous of the legion of mollusks is the black abalone, found in crannies near low tide mark. It is greenish black on the outside, smooth except for the lines of growth, has five to nine holes and is markedly convex. It is, in fact, a sort of limpet with multiple keyholes. Due to its protected status within the Reserve, the black abalone is again becoming plentiful at the Point. Red abalone, a larger species, is not commonly seen at Point Lobos, however, during heavy winter storms they are sometimes dislodged and cast ashore.

True limpets are common. On Punta de los Lobos Marinos the plate, shield, dingy, rough, and file limpets are found. Shells of the white cap, pure white and conical, are often washed up on the beach. The animals dwell under rocks. Above the limpets in the spray zone are the littorines, already noted.

In the tide pools the commonest sea snails are the black and brown turbans, upward of an inch and a half high, usually aggregated in cracks of the rocks. *Crepidula*, the slipper shell, is often found adhering to the turbans. The blue top, *Calliostoma*, is sometimes common. More colorful, however, are the slugs, or *nudibranchs*, which are devoid of shell and vary greatly in size and tint. One of the showiest is the yellow to orange sea lemon, *Anisodoris*, likely to be found among laminarian kelps; *Triopha* shows orange markings against white; while the small *Hopkinsia* is bright rose. Some of the small aeolid nudibranchs, under a magnifier, are among the most beautiful of all animals.

The chitons (*ki-tons*) or "sea cradles" have the habits of limpets, but instead of a single shell they have eight separate shells, each one perfectly articulated to the next, like a coat of mail. They cling tenaciously to rocks, but are found in a great variety of places. *Katharina* and *Nuttallina* live on more or less exposed surfaces; the strikingly beautiful lined chiton on more sheltered ones. Many chitons, including the blue and gray ones, remain attached to the undersides of stones and only forage at night. While some adult chitons are less than half an inch long, the dark red, giant chiton may get to be a foot long or even longer. It is found among kelps in the deepest pools, its shell completely hidden by a tough, plush-like skin. Chitons feed on minute plants and kelps which they rasp into their mouths with file-like tongues.

Although worms are legion, they are not likely to engage the attention, with perhaps one exception, the feather duster, which lives in a tough, parchment-like tube which adheres to the rocks. The color of the feathery gills is purple, wine color, tawny or whitish. Small serpulids with brilliant red feathery gills and twisted lime tubes are frequently very numerous. Predaceous crawlers, hidden in sponges, mussel beds, sand, or rock crannies, come out mostly at night. Segmented worms swallow smaller worms and crustacea, and are in turn devoured by ribbon worms. Giant *Nereis*, which can be as much as three feet in length, have not been found on the Point but undoubtedly are in residence, hidden within deep burrows, among loose rock.

The foregoing is, of course, only a very sketchy picture of Point Lobos intertidal life, touching only a few of the more colorful highlights of the richly varied life that can be seen there. This rich heritage of life forms — rare in all the world — should be carefully preserved for the benefit of those who love the sea, and for those who would study undisturbed natural conditions.

For those who desire to become more thoroughly acquainted with the principal types of intertidal animal life there are two excellent books: *Between Pacific Tides* by E.F. Ricketts and Jack Calvin, and *Seashore Animals of the Pacific Coast* by M.E. Johnson and H.J. Snook.

Hemigrapsus nudus

Porcelain or flat crab, Petrolisthes cinctipes

Bat star, Patiria miniata

Sunflower star, Pyncnapodia heliathoides

Abalone meat drying on racks overlooking Whalers Cove, 1905.

X

History at Point Lobos

Aubrey Drury/V. Aubrey Neasham

Indian Use of Point Lobos

FOR MANY CENTURIES—probably for several thousand years—Point Lobos was occupied by Indians. Archeological evidence is somewhat scanty (mainly shell deposits and bedrock mortars), but it is clear that the Point was often visited by Indians and that more or less permanent settlements were established near the mouths of San Jose Creek and Gibson Creek, the only places in this vicinity where fresh water was available on a reliable basis. Definite Indian shell mounds are located at these two sites, indicating a more continuous, permanent kind of settlement than is suggested by other shell deposits within the Reserve. The two main sites were probably at least the spring and summer residence areas of groups that had winter villages somewhere inland, in more sheltered valleys.

Temporary or "intermittent" camp sites of Indians are found at nineteen places along the six miles of shore line. Most of these sites appear to have been little more than overnight fishing stations, which were revisited year after year by Indians from the interior, to gather abalones, mussels, and other mollusks. There are five localities on the Point where mortar holes for grinding seeds and acorns—probably of the coast live oak—occur in association with the shell deposits.

From examination of the mounds, shell deposits and other remains, it seems likely that many of these sites were centuries old when Europeans first reached the California coast. It is not definitely known whether the Indians were more closely related to those of the San Francisco Bay region, or to the Channel Islanders, or whether they formed a distinctive group with the adjacent mainland peoples.

Much of what we do know about the ancient habitation of this area is based upon the findings published in "An Archaeological Reconnaissance of Point Lobos," written by Waldo R. Wedel, an anthropologist from the University of California at Berkeley.

Early Exploration

EARLY EXPLORERS, including Cabrillo and Ferrelo, undoubtedly saw Point Lobos from the sea, though it does not seem to have been specifically mentioned in any of their journals. Sebastian Viscaíno passed close by several times in 1602-3 and at one point his ships entered Carmel Bay, and some of the Spaniards went ashore, camping near the mouth of Rio del

V. Aubrey Neasham supervised the prolific historical research program of the California Division of Parks as carried out in California during the 1930s under the auspices of the Federal Work Projects Administration. From 1934 to 1953 he was Regional Historian for the National Park Service in the Southwest and West. In 1953 he joined the California Division of Beaches and Parks where he established continuing programs of historical and archeological work, and supervised development of masterplans that have guided the preservation and development of historical resources at many places including Bodie, Columbia, Monterey, and the gold discovery site at Coloma. Since 1964 he has been chairman of the Department of Environmental Resources at Sacramento State College.

Carmelo, which Viscaíno named in honor of three Carmelite friars who accompanied him. It seems quite possible that Viscaíno himself, or at least some of his men, actually set foot upon Point Lobos.

The exploring party of Don Gaspar de Portolá marched by here in October 1769; and Sergeant José Francisco Ortega, the "pathfinder" of the expedition, made a careful study of the coastline south of Carmel River. For a time Portolá's men were camped upon the banks of San José Creek, and his livestock grazed upon the lush grasses there.

In 1771 Mission San Carlos Borromeo was moved from Monterey to its present site close beside the Carmel River, with Point Lobos in view to the southwest. Padre Junípero Serra, who was a great walker, doubtless visited the Point many times.

The native vaqueros of Carmel Mission ran large herds of cattle in the Point Lobos area from an early date, and the padres claimed the land on behalf of their Indians. Cattle grazing was the first real use made by the Spaniards of this region. Old records tell of the Mission herdsmen lassoing bears near San Jose Creek, while driving their cattle.

It is likely that the name Point Lobos (Punta de los Lobos Marinos, Point of the Sea Wolves) was given in Spanish times.

Ownership of Point Lobos

IN 1833, the missions of California were placed under civil or secular control. As a result most of the mission lands were thrown open to ownership and settlement by private citizens. On July 30, 1834, Juan B. Alvarado was given a grant, Rancho el Sur, which may have included a portion of the lands in the vicinity of Point Lobos. When Teodoro Gonzales, on September 2, 1835, applied for the rancho of Sur Chiquito, the map which he submitted shows that the grant for which he applied definitely included Point Lobos.

The grant which remained valid, however, was that given on April 16, 1839, to Don Marcelino Escobar, a prominent official of Monterey. This baronial domain of the Rancho San Jose y Sur Chiquito, consisting roughly of two leagues, was bounded on the north by the Carmel River, on the east by the mountains, on the south by Palo Colorado Canyon, and on the west by the Pacific Ocean. All subsequent title claims concerning Point Lobos stem from this grant which was confirmed by the Mexican government in 1840.

After 1840 and until the State of California secured title in 1933 literally scores of claimants tried to prove the legitimacy of their various claims. As a result the story of these claims involves a certain amount of mystery and intrigue, and the attendant litigation has been both complex and confusing.

Two of Don Marcelino's sons, Juan and Augustin, seem to have obtained possession of the rancho shortly after the grant to their father. However that may have occurred, they in turn deeded it to Doña Josefa de Abrego on August 26, 1841. That señora, holding power of attorney from her husband to buy and sell land, paid $250, one-half in merchandise, for the rancho.

The next step in the process of conveyance remains somewhat of a mystery. Somehow the rancho was deeded to a group of soldiers from the Monterey presidio on January 16, 1843, by Doña Josefa. It seems that they paid nothing for it, and yet the records leave no doubt that she deeded it to them. There is a legend that a gambler once lost the rancho at cards. Perhaps this is where the legend came from: Did Doña Josefa, acting in the power of attorney for her husband, Don Jose de Abrego, turn the property over to the soldiers in payment of her husband's gambling debts? That story has been told of Don Marcelino Escobar, but it appears that it was Don Jose who gambled and lost a rancho rather than Don Marcelino.

The soldiers of the presidio, about ten in number, held the land in their names until June 7, 1844, when they turned it over to their superior officer, General Jose Castro, prominent in the annals of California history for his opposition to the American invasion. As late as 1848, Castro was given quit claim deeds by the soldiers concerned.

In any case, regardless of who held legal title to the land, it is certain that the Point Lobos area was used for grazing cattle. As a matter of fact Don Marcelino Escobar's grant, in 1839, specifically mentions cattle grazing.

The annexation of California by the United States, in 1848, resulted in the establishment of a land commission to review all private claims in California. Thus it was that Jose Castro filed a petition as claimant to the Rancho San Jose y Sur Chiquito on February 2, 1853. The Board of Land Commissioners rendered a decree rejecting Castro's claim on August 28, 1855, thereby rendering invalid, seemingly, the original claim of 1839. Castro's claim was appealed to the United States District Court, where it remained for years in doubt.

To complicate matters still more—in 1854, about a year before the rejection of his claim by the United States Land Commission, General Castro sold out to Joseph S. Emery and Abner Bassett for $750. As a result it was they who carried on the fight for title to the rancho. Before the final decision of the court, Bassett died, in 1874, leaving his estate to his wife and eight children. His undivided one-half of the 8,818.56-acre Rancho San Jose y Sur Chiquito was then appraised at $15,000.

Up to this point the title claim to the Escobar grant is relatively simple and can be followed without overwhelming difficulty. However, other claims began to be put forward at an early date, and these conflicting deeds and questions of squatters' rights began to entangle the Castro claim in an almost impossible maze.

The earliest conflicting claim was that of the Escobar heirs. Only two of the children, Juan and Augustin, had deeded the rancho to Doña Josefa de Abrego in 1841. However, there were other sons and daughters, and later grandchildren, who claimed a portion of Don Marcelino's grant. All of these heirs together agreed, on March 25, 1859, to give one Delos R. Ashley, an attorney, one-half of the rancho if he would get it back for them. Later, in 1860 and 1861, these same heirs sold a portion of what they claimed to Mathew G. Ireland, who had on March 12, 1859, bought a quit claim deed from the Abrego family. December 1, 1877, found one-ninth of the rancho "sold" by the Escobar heirs to Adam Joseph Kopsch. In addition to the above claims, a Sidney S. Johnson claimed that Emery and Bassett had agreed earlier to give him one-third of the rancho. The squatters' claims were almost too numerous to mention.

By 1880, when a suit was filed in the United States District Court to settle the respective claims, the following people claimed the land: Joseph S. Emery, one-half; the Bassett Estate, one-half; Sidney S. Johnson, one-third; W. Van Dyke, the successor of Kopsch, one-ninth; the heirs of D. R. Ashley, one-fourth: W. T. Baggett, who had bought one-half of the Ashley interest, one-fourth; and Joseph W. Gregg, who had bought the Ireland claim of about 1,000 acres north of San Jose Creek.

The final agreement, recorded on June 5, 1882, which was subject to the confirmation of the Castro claim by the United States, found the claimants receiving the following percentages: Ashley heirs, one-ninth; W. T. Baggett, one-ninth; J. S. Emery, two-ninths; Bassett Estate, two-ninths; Sidney S. Johnson, two-ninths; and W. Van Dyke, one-ninth. Gregg's claim to the land north of San Jose Creek was later recognized, as were the claims of some twenty-seven others, mostly squatters.

An agreement had been reached, then, between those who claimed portions of the Rancho San Jose y Sur Chiquito. Only the confirmation of the Castro claim remained in the way of those claimants having the portions which they claimed. As yet, with the exception of Gregg and the squatters, there seemed to be only undivided interests.

The Castro appeal was finally won, in 1882, in the case of *The United States of America versus Joseph S. Emery, Nathan W. Spaulding, with the will annexed of Abner Bassett, as successors in the interest of Jose Castro, deceased, the claimant herein.* The title was confirmed on December 24, 1885, and the patent was signed by President Grover Cleveland on May 4, 1888. After thirty-five years of doubt and uncertainty all those people whose land titles were based on the validity of the Castro claim were at last recognized as the undisputed legal owners of their various parcels of Point Lobos land.

Commercial Activity at Point Lobos

DURING MUCH OF THIS PERIOD of litigation, Point Lobos was a center of a maritime industry. Carmelito Cove (now known as Whalers Cove), though small, offered a base of operations for whaling, which began there in 1861 or 1862. Some twenty Portuguese used the cove as their base. Whalers Knoll, above the old quarry, was used to sight the whales. When captured and killed, a whale was brought to the derricks and tackles in the cove, where it was cut up in the water. Iron cauldrons set in stone were used to boil the whale oil. The flames and smoke of the quays, the shrilling of seagulls, the shouting of men, and all the attendant excitement were in marked contrast to the peaceful locale—the small frame cottages of the whalers; the pigs and goats and cows browsing roundabout, and the neat little gardens, which were planted mostly to corn and pumpkins. Today, all that remains of the whaling industry, which was abandoned in 1884, is an old iron cauldron, a pair of anchors, and the lonely, weather-bleached whaler's cottage beneath the gigantic cypress that long-time residents say was planted beside the cottage about 1875. Visitors to Whalers Cove may also notice the derrick rings set into one of the rocks out in the bay that are also said to date from the era of whalers.

On September 6, 1888, shortly after President Cleveland signed the patent to Rancho San Jose y Sur Chiquito, the various undisputed owners of land at Point Lobos (with the exception of Gregg and the squatters, whose claims did not depend on the Castro claim) banded together and sold their interests to the Carmelo Land and Coal Company, a corporation, for the sum of one dollar. They, of course, held shares in the company equivalent to their interests in the land. Thus, for the first time in almost half a century, the Rancho San Jose y Sur Chiquito, including Point Lobos, came under one ownership.

Cannery Point and the abalone cannery at Whalers Cove from the air, May 22, 1931.

By then it had been determined that the hills back of the Point contained coal deposits that were considered valuable. Shortly after its formation in 1888 the Carmelo Land and Coal Company set out to exploit these deposits. A railroad was built from the mine to the county road, and a coal chute was set up in order to transfer the coal from the road to the north side of Carmelo Cove. The annual report of the State Mineralogist in 1890 tells us that more than 720 feet of the coal mine had been retimbered, and that the coal in three distinct veins varied in thickness from two to nine feet. A hoisting engine, built at a cost of $10,000, was to be used in bringing the coal to the surface. Chinese laborers were employed to do most of the actual mining.

However, by 1896 adverse market conditions combined with the expense of operation to close the mine down, and it has remained closed ever since.

Granite was quarried at Point Lobos and to this day the old quarry site, close beside Whalers Cove, is clear evidence that a considerable amount of rock was taken out. It is said that both the old United States Mint in San Francisco and the jail at Colton Hall, Monterey were built from Point Lobos granite.

Prospecting or mining for gold at Point Lobos caused occasional flurries of excitement. In 1863, a group of prominent citizens formed the San Carlos Gold Mining Company. Though it was capitalized to the extent of $50,000, it ended in failure. In 1907, prospectors were given permission to enter Point Lobos and explore for mineral wealth. The expedition turned up no interesting prospects and was the last recorded attempt to tap mineral resources at Point Lobos.

Exploitation of ocean resources was more successful, however. The Indians had been gathering seafood along the shore of Point Lobos for hundreds and thousands of years. Later explorers also fished there. Chinese coal miners also did some fishing at Point Lobos. The United States Surveyor

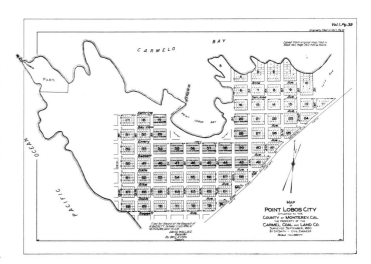

General's 1885 map of the Rancho San Jose y Sur Chiquito shows several Chinese fishermen's huts near the beach of Carmelo Cove, as well as one just south of the present Reserve boundary.

During the 1890s, Japanese fishermen were brought to Point Lobos to help develop an abalone canning industry. Using long hooks and nets, the Japanese at first fished mainly near the shore in water not more than ten feet deep. Later, diving suits were used, both from the shore and from the boats in deeper water.

An abalone cannery was established at the site of the old whaling station, near the foot of the quarry cliff. Traces of abalone shell, brilliant with color, remain today as reminders that many cases of canned abalone were packed here for shipment to the Orient, for that is where most of them found their way. The cannery continued in operation until 1928, and in 1933 the buildings were demolished by the state authori-

Point Lobos City, or Carmelito, was laid out by the Carmel Coal and Land Company in 1890. It consisted of nearly 1,000 lots, many of them just twenty-five feet wide. In 1908 A. M. Allan gained control of the financially troubled company, took up residence at Point Lobos, and began a thirty-year fight to buy back the lots and abandon the old subdivision. In 1927, with auto touring rapidly becoming popular, Allan hired a plant pathologist to study the impact of human visitors on the cypress grove. The pathologist quoted Allan as saying, "It is my hope to preserve this property in its natural state for the enjoyment of those who appreciate nature, provided that such use will not get beyond control and become a menace to the property itself."

A. M. Allan

IN 1896, Joseph Emery met A. M. Allan in Oakland, and interested him in Point Lobos. Allan was familiar with the practical aspects of coal mining, and it was largely this factor that led Allan to purchase 640 acres of the coal mining company's land at Point Lobos. The date of the purchase was January 14, 1898.

Allan held the land in his name despite a series of suits with various parties, including members of the Carmelo Land and Coal Company and the Monterey County supervisors. He also set out to buy back all of the lots that had been sold as part of the Carmelito subdivision project.

Allan lived in his ranch house at Point Lobos from 1897 until his death in 1930 at the age of seventy. Born in Pennsylvania, he took his first job at the age of twelve as a mule driver in a Pennsylvania coal mine. He worked his way through school and finally graduated from the University of Illinois in 1884. Later he became a race track architect and constructor. In some of this activity he was associated with Lucky Baldwin, notably in building the early Santa Anita track. Allan came to California to build the Ingleside track and also constructed tracks at Ascot Park, Los Angeles, and at Tanforan and Emeryville in the San Francisco Bay region. He was an elder in the Presbyterian Church. Besides managing his holdings here, Allan was a banker and head of a fish canning company.

During the Allan regime, dairying and a limited amount of farming were part of the economic background of the Point Lobos area. Across the road from the Reserve there stands a dairy operated by Allan heirs. Fruit trees remain about some of the old houses. Lumbering, on a very small scale, had some part in the activities of the neighborhood. Gibson Creek, forming the south boundary of the Reserve, gets its name from a Mr. Gibson, who hauled redwood posts out of that canyon, above the part now in state ownership.

ties in order to return the area to a more natural condition.

In 1890-91 the Carmelo Land and Coal Company subdivided part of Point Lobos and attempted to establish a residential and resort community there. This speculative development was first named Point Lobos City, and later came to be known as Carmelito. It was made up of twenty-five-foot- and fifty-foot-wide lots. Mrs. Robert Louis Stevenson and her sister, Mrs. Sanchez, are both said to have owned one or more of these lots. Quite a number of lots were sold, but the projected village did not become a reality. Fortunately, Carmelito remained a ghost town as shown by the revised plat of the town filed on May 29, 1891. A rigid gridiron pattern of streets was laid out close beside Whalers Cove, which was then known as Carmelo or Carmelito Cove. The main street was called Bassett Avenue, and other streets bore the names of Emery, Doble, and Baggett. In the map filed, a reservation marked Point Lobos Park was indicated on Cypress Point.

Establishment of the Reserve

UNDER THE ALLAN OWNERSHIP, Point Lobos was maintained intact, without further subdivision. Visitors had resorted to the Point for outings even as early as the Mexican regime; and now they came in increasing numbers to see the famous cypress trees and the scenic shore. A toll-gate was established, carriages and automobiles paying toll for admission. Care of the cypress trees became a primary concern of the owners. Artists and scientists resorted to the Point, as did thousands of other lovers of nature. With the development of motion pictures, a number of producing companies came here "on location"—the first in 1916.

The proposal that Point Lobos should be made a public reserve was broached at the time Carmelito was laid out. The subdividers, as has been noted, marked the outer cypress-crowned headland Point Lobos Park. Later it was declared by some that this property had been given to the public at that time—1891.

Dr. David Starr Jordan, in an official report of 1880, informed the government that the Carmel Bay area, including Point Lobos, was in his opinion the most picturesque spot on the Pacific Coast. Shortly after 1900 a meeting was held in the little museum at Pacific Grove, with a number of scientists and Sierra Club members present, and the preservation of Point Lobos and Cypress Point as national parks or reserves was discussed.

In August 1909, G. Frederick Schwarz, noted forester who had made a study of the Monterey cypress groves, wrote to A. M. Allan suggesting, "You might perhaps see your way clear to add your beautiful cypress holdings at Point Lobos to those at Pescadero Point, if the latter were established as a State Park."

Impetus was given the discussion of a park here when, in 1919, the Carmel-San Simeon highway was started, and increasing travel came this way.

There grew out of the Save-the-Redwoods movement a statewide park program for California. This was developed from a meeting in San Francisco, January 5, 1925, at which time Point Lobos was prominently mentioned as an area which should be included in the State Park System. The Save-the-Redwoods League had several times definitely considered the possibility of preserving a representative grove of Monterey cypress, as at Point Lobos.

A meeting of members of the league and other citizens was held in the Palace Hotel, San Francisco, on December 9, 1926, to advance the acquisition of Point Lobos as a public reserve. As a result of this meeting, Duncan McDuffie, on behalf of the group, later in December engaged Frederick Law Olmsted, internationally known landscape architect, to make an investigation and report as to the areas most worthy of preservation. The report rendered on April 15, 1927, formed the basis of future plans for a statewide system of state parks.

In his official report (the State Park Survey), published in 1929, Frederick Law Olmsted declared the Point Lobos project to be of primary importance, terming the point "the most outstanding example on the coast of California of picturesque rock and surf scenery in combination with unique vegetation, including typical Monterey cypress."

Point Lobos was acquired by the state according to a plan devised by Newton B. Drury, who was serving simultaneously as Secretary to the Save-the-Redwoods League and as Acquisition Officer for the State Division of Parks. Matching funds from the State Park Bond Act were available for purchase of the Point Lobos area if private funds could be found in equal amounts. Mr. Drury pointed out that State Park Bond funds expended on the Prairie Creek Redwoods project amounted to less than the one-half stipulated in the State Park Bond Act. The Save-the-Redwoods League had contributed much more than one-half of the total amount needed for the Prairie Creek Redwoods project and the resulting "matching credit" established there could be used to justify the issuance of bonds for the purchase of Point Lobos. (Prairie Creek Redwoods State Park had been acquired through the instrumentality of the Save-the-Redwoods League largely by means of very generous gifts from Edward S. Harkness.)

On October 19, 1932, the State Park Finance Board authorized issue of state park bonds for the purchase of approximately 400 acres at Point Lobos. Transfer of title to the State was made on February 8, 1933. The amount involved was $631,000. According to agreement with the Allan family, a portion of the Cypress Headland was to be considered a gift, and dedicated as a memorial to A. M. Allan and his wife, Satie Morgan Allan.

It was recognized that the acquisition of Point Lobos as part of the State Park System presented an unusual opportunity for its "preservation and protection as a reserve, accessible to the public in such ways as permit its enjoyment without impairing its excellence—safeguarding for all time its unique inspirational, educational and scientific interest." Such was the program of the Point Lobos Association which, from 1927 to 1933, under the leadership of Mrs. Robert Hunter, devoted study to means of conservation.

Carrying on this program, the organizational meeting of the Advisory Committee on Protection and Use of Point Lobos (a committee of the Save-the-Redwoods League) was held on November 29, 1933, at the Custodian's Lodge, Point Lobos. Acting on the advice of this committee the State Park Commission asked Dr. John C. Merriam to select a special scientific advisory committee that could undertake a detailed study of Point Lobos. This study was financed by the Carnegie Corporation and the Save-the-Redwoods League and required two years to complete. The results were brought together in one comprehensive, detailed study that was then published by the Carnegie Institution of Washington, D.C. With the approval of the State Park Commission, the Olmsted Brothers firm of landscape architects was then hired by the advisory committee to do a master plan for development and administration of Point Lobos.

Both the original study and the subsequent master plan were widely considered to be the finest work of their kind and were used as models for similar projects in other parts of the nation. On March 1, 1936, the Point Lobos Advisory Committee of the Save-the-Redwoods League submitted its report and policy recommendations to the State Park Commission. With minor modifications both of these documents were adopted by the State Park Commission and have served since that time as the backbone of all policy decisions regarding Point Lobos State Reserve.

William Colby was president of the Sierra Club and a leader in the effort to establish a statewide system of parks. As a resident of the Monterey area and Chairman of the State Park Commission, he played an important role in negotiations that led to the creation of Point Lobos State Reserve.

A. M. Allan.

The south shore as seen from the pine woods.

Diver photographing marine life in the giant macrocystis.

XI

The Marine Reserve

Penelope Hermes

Penelope Hermes, a journalist and underwater photographer, has been diving at Point Lobos for several years, and recently completed a guide to the underwater life of the marine reserve as part of her work toward a masters degree in journalism. She also holds a masters degree in science education, has taught high school biology, and worked as a medical technician. Articles by Miss Hermes have appeared in *Audubon* and *Canadian Nature* magazines.

AS YOU HIKE THE TRAILS of Point Lobos you are only seeing half a reserve. Out of sight, beneath the ocean surrounding this reserve is another Point Lobos, just as spectacular and even more colorful.

Here, within a 775-acre marine reserve at Point Lobos, giant forests of kelp 70 feet tall soar upward from the rocky reefs. Hundreds of blue rockfish shoal in the treetops of the kelp, while below lingcod and convict fish roam the reefs. Brightly colored sponges, anemones and rare hydrocorals carpet the bottom rocks. Within the Reserve's Bluefish Cove a branch of the Carmel Submarine Canyon — an underwater "Grand Canyon" — begins its 10,000-foot descent.

But most of these wonders were unknown when the State Park Commission resolved to set aside this marine reserve October 16, 1959. Then park officials saw the proposed reserve as a buffer zone to protect the land portion of Point Lobos. With deepening concern, they had watched the rich intertidal animal and seaweed life of the reserve dwindle. Tidepools looked barren. A Department of Fish and Game official reported that abalones, which once clustered along the shoreline, were "cleaned out."

Visitors were partly to blame. Scientists and other tidepool collectors were taking too many specimens. Busloads of visiting schoolchildren, armed with plastic buckets, carted away more of the multicolored starfish and sea animals. Some visitors carelessly turned over tidepool rocks leaving their inhabitants to die in the sun. There were occasional reports of deliberate vandalism and harassment of shore animals. Boaters and fishermen roamed the offshore waters without restriction.

The new sport of SCUBA-diving, blossoming in the fifties, brought a surge of "wet-suited" divers exploring underwater in Carmel Bay and at Point Lobos. Although some were scientists and underwater photographers, most speared fish or collected scallops and abalone. At nearby San Jose Creek Beach, souveniring underwater tourists waded ashore with "goodie bags" stuffed with sea shells, branching hydrocorals and gorgonians. Even today all too little is known about the impact of divers on underwater environments.

To adequately protect Point Lobos and its underwater resources, park officials realized that they must extend their jurisdiction to the intertidal and subtidal lands surrounding the reserve. Throughout 1959, representatives of the Department of Parks and Recreation met with diving organizations, the Point Lobos League, and other conservation groups in order to draft regulations that would allow limited access to the reserve while still protecting it.

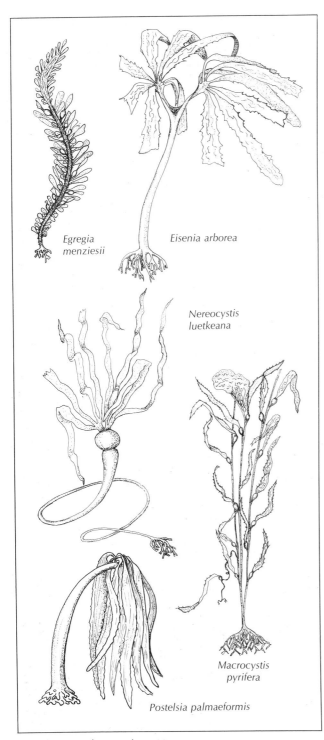

Egregia
menziesii

Eisenia arborea

Nereocystis
luetkeana

Macrocystis
pyrifera

Postelsia palmaeformis

Line drawings by Penelope Hermes.

Finally on April 15, 1960, the Department of Parks and Recreation received title to 775 acres of tidal and submerged lands surrounding Point Lobos. The nation's first underwater reserve was a reality.

A Dive in the Underwater Reserve

THE DIVER who visits Point Lobos begins his voyage amid the surface canopy of kelp in Whalers Cove. Here curious sea otters, furry, five-foot-long mammals, often pop up to stare at him and then, wary of the diver's approach, dive and disappear in a liquid movement.

Once underwater, the diver swims from the shallows down to thirty feet through a jungle of red and brown seaweeds.[1] He fins among pillars of twisted kelp stalks, surrounded by rockfish so tame that he can almost reach out and touch them. Around him stretches an underseascape of pinnacles and plateaus, remnants of former granite headlands eroded by the waves. The wiry red coralline seaweeds that carpet the reefs below him provide a hiding place for small sea animals. Yellow feather-duster worms (*Eudistylia*) and saucer-sized anemones (*Tealia*) blossom from the rock crevices. Speckled orange and yellow bat stars (*Patiria*) scavenge on sandy plains between the reefs.

Sometimes a plump and playful harbor seal will swim up to a diver and tug at his flippers. If the diver stops to look into a crevice the seal may snuggle up next to him and peer in too.

As the diver moves deeper down the reef, daylight dims and disappears. One by one the warm colors of the spectrum turn to gray. Below three feet, red sponges fade; by ten feet orange starfish lose their brilliance; at thirty feet clusters of yellow bryozoans begin to gray and the diver swims through a twilight world of muted colors. Between thirty and sixty feet he planes over a forest within a forest, where a scattered shrubbery of palm-tree kelps some five feet tall anchor to the reefs. With increasing depth this palm-tree forest of *Eisenia*[2] kelp thins out and disappears.

Below fifty feet there is not enough sunlight for most seaweeds to grow, and ninety percent of the life the diver sees is animal. Yellow sponges, strawberry anemones (*Corynactis*) and brittle bryozoans so overgrow granite walls that not an inch of bare rock is visible. As he enters the darkening deeps below seventy feet, the diver leaves the kelp forests behind and descends past rock walls covered with animals. If he switches on his underwater flashlight, these walls explode into color—neon red, orange, yellow. Colorful starfish and lemon sea slugs glow in its beam. Seemingly black or gray anemones (*Tealia*) suddenly blaze red.

Sometimes a diver is startled by the sleek missile of a California sea lion gliding by. Typically these sea lions swoop in to investigate a diver, then quickly speed away.

If he descends below 100 feet, the diver sinks into a chill monochrome world where the air he breathes seems thick as cream and every kick is tiring. Animal growth is even richer here. White clusters of four-foot-tall anemones (*Metridium*) cling to ledges like ghostly toadstools. Small patches of gorgonians extend their feeding tentacles to catch a fallout of plankton. Scores of sea cucumbers (*Stichopus*) prowl among

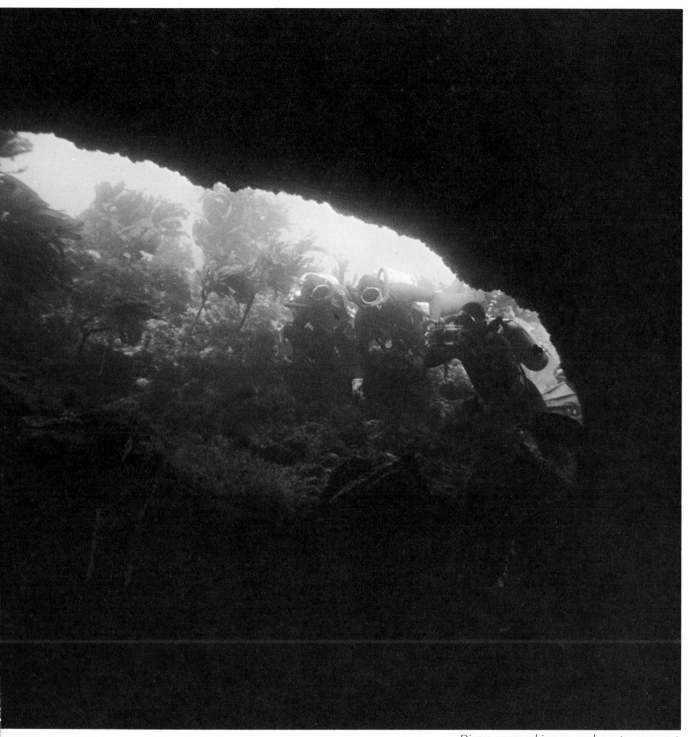

Divers approaching an underwater cave cut
into the rock by surf of another age.

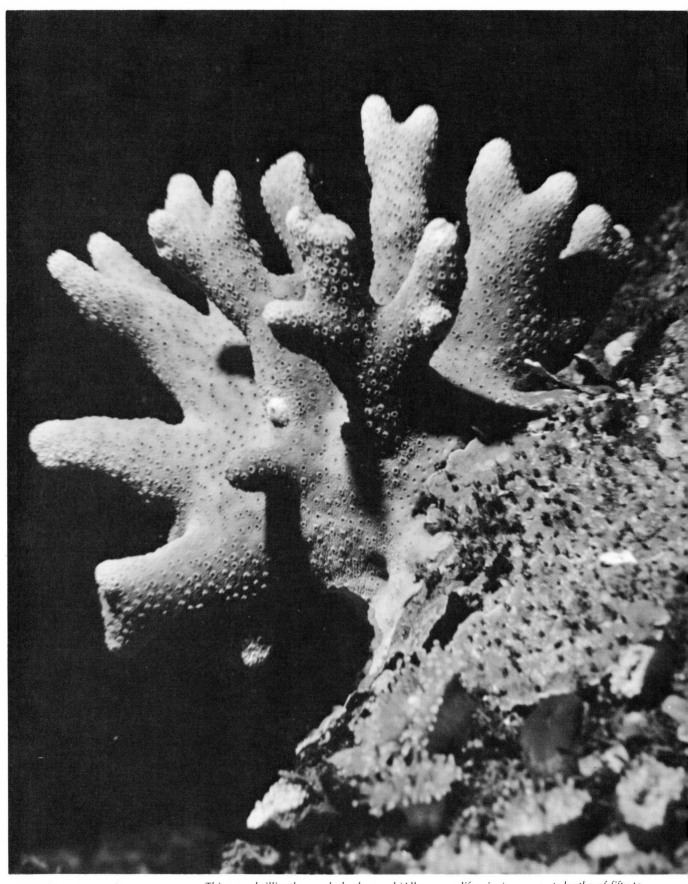

This rare, brilliantly purple hydrocoral (Allopora californica) occurs at depths of fifty to eighty feet and is a favorite with underwater photographers.

the few scattered red seaweeds looking for edible debris. At this depth a diver's breathing time is limited to minutes; soon he must kick upslope toward the warmth and color of the sunlit kelp forests.

A Panorama of Underwater Life

THE FEAST OF LIFE that divers find underwater makes tide-pools and the fringes of the sea seem like deserts. Intertidal animals are limited to the hardy select few that can withstand being battered by waves and alternately dehydrated or pickled in brine between tides. By contrast, subtidal animals, living underwater where temperature and other conditions are relatively stable, flourish abundantly. Immersed in a rich broth of plankton, larger sea animals like feather-duster worms and barnacles have only to reach out and take the food they need. Here only space is at a premium.

The plants and animals that flourish in this marine reserve are a part of a life zone that extends from San Diego to the Gulf of Alaska. Not only are sea temperatures fairly uniform throughout this zone, but many of the same kinds of seaweeds and invertebrates occur throughout its length. More kinds of starfish are found here than in any other comparable undersea area—some ninety-two species. The world's largest starfish, the bat star (*Pycnopodia*), which grows as large as four feet across, is common in the Reserve. Point Lobos also boasts some of the world's largest mollusks—sea snails and their relatives. These include: the gumboot chiton (*Cryptochiton stelleri*), a foot-long chiton with eight plates instead of a shell embedded in the surface of its body; the giant keyhole limpet (*Megathura crenulata*), a limpet which covers its bowl-shaped shell with a black skin; and Lewis' moon snail (*Polinices lewisii*), one of the world's largest snails. An amazing number and variety of nudibranchs (sea snails that lack shells) occur in the Reserve; divers often see foot-long lemon sea slugs (*Anisodoris nobilis*).

Greenlings, surf perches, sculpins and rockfishes are

An eighteen-inch-long sea cucumber.

Juvenile macrocystis

The tentacles of the tube anemone undulate slowly and gracefully with the underwater currents.

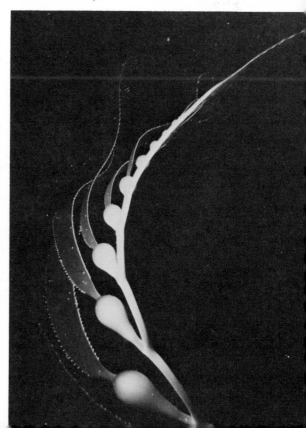

common residents of Point Lobos and this region. More than fifty species of rockfish (*Sebastodes*) are found along the Pacific Coast. At Point Lobos the blue, black, black-and-yellow and copper rockfishes are common.

At Point Lobos the ranges of many undersea animals overlap. Sheepshead fish, gorgonian corals and chestnut cowrie shells, typical of Southern California waters, occur here as well as solitary corals, giant *Metridium* anemones and orange sea cucumbers (*Cucumaria*) typical of waters north of California. Many marine invertebrates found intertidally in the North Pacific are only found subtidally at Point Lobos and along the Central California coast.

Most of this rich assemblage of life is centered in kelp beds. Sea lions, sea otters, and fish hunt for food in them; sea urchins, abalones, turban snails and other undersea vegetarians browse on the kelp blades. Young crabs and many other juvenile invertebrates find a protected nursery in the root-like holdfasts that anchor giant kelps. Scientists have counted more than 10,000 invertebrates large enough to see with the naked eye in a single holdfast.

These kelps, largest of our brown seaweeds, parallel the Pacific Coast in large and extensive beds several miles long. Kelps and other seaweeds growing subtidally along the Monterey Peninsula are particularly tall and luxuriant because of the abundant minerals dissolved in seawater here. These minerals also darken the red pigments that color certain seaweeds. As a result, the Atlantic Coast counterparts of these kelps seem pale and anemic by comparison.

Seasons in the Sea

THE LUSH SEAWEED BEDS, the number and variety of undersea animals and fish at Point Lobos, are a result of the seasonal upwelling of minerals that fertilize the ocean along our coast. In spring and summer, northwesterly winds push the surface ocean water seaward. This water is replaced by cold, mineral-rich water from the depths. Nitrates and phosphates, present in the upwelling water, spur a growth of microscopic seaweeds that turns the sunlit waters green. Soon

Beaded anemone (Telia lofatensus)

vast numbers of tiny invertebrates move in to feed on these green pastures, and they in turn are harvested by larger invertebrates and fish. In fact, the hatching of many fish eggs is timed to take advantage of this seasonal food supply. Divers who go underwater at Point Lobos during the upwelling season find themselves swimming in a rich broth of life so thick that they cannot see their hands in front of their facemasks. In late summer a change in winds and ocean currents ends upwelling. With the rich broth of animals finally consumed the underwater panorama again becomes visible.

Marine Reserves and the Future

THE MARINE RESERVE at Point Lobos is valuable for its scenic qualities, but it is even more valuable because it preserves a marine wilderness complete with its unique collection of sea life. It protects the richest area of undersea life in Central California, and is a sanctuary to endangered species including sea otters and certain rare hydrocorals.

It is a reservoir of juvenile fish and invertebrates that could repopulate adjoining underseascapes should those less protected areas suffer some ecological disaster.

It provides a control area where scientists can study the health of our coastal waters, make long-term observations on sea life and let experiments percolate relatively undisturbed. Without such an area, scientists would be less able to measure the blighting effects of ocean pollution, or other effects of man's intrusion into the sea.

In the ten or so years since the marine reserve was set aside, more than a dozen scientific studies have been done in its waters. Scientists have charted the seasonal distribution of kelp beds, probed the habits of sea otters, measured the growth of coralline seaweeds and studied the reproductive life of hydrocorals. Currently a group of divers is systematically mapping and surveying the fauna and flora, as well as the physical terrain of the entire marine reserve.

Commenting on the need for underwater parks and reserves, William Penn Mott Jr., Director of the Department of Parks and Recreation, pointed out in 1968 that, "Time is running out on our ability to set aside marine parks and reserves. This now is as important as were the deliberations in 1934 by our department in preserving the redwoods. We have only one Pacific Coast and the rest of the nation is watching what we do with this resource."

In 1969 marine reserves were established at Salt Point Ranch north of San Francisco, at Torrey Pines near San Diego, and at Julia Pfeiffer Burns State Park in Big Sur. But this may be just a beginning. Each year the aesthetic and scientific values of these reserves attract more attention. Clearly we have just begun to understand and enjoy the fascinating underwater world along the California coastline.

---

1 — Brown seaweeds, common from the shallows down to sixty feet in the reserve, include: *Macrocystis, Nereocystis, Eisenia, Pterygophora, Laminaria* and *Dictyoneurum*. Red seaweeds; *Gigartina, Calliarthron* and *Botryoglossum* are common on the reefs at thirty feet; *Fryeella, Opuntiella* and *Weeksia* are more common below fifty-foot depths.

2 — *Eisenia* is a rare kelp along this coast; thus far Point Lobos is the only locale between Southern California and Vancouver where it has been found. In the Point Lobos area *Eisenia* grows only at fifteen feet or more of depth and therefore can only be seen by divers.